Lost in Evolution

Lost in Evolution

Exploring Humanity's Path in Asia

Hiroto Kawabata

TECHNICAL ADVISOR Yousuke Kaifu

TRANSLATED BY
Dana Lewis

Japan Publishing Industry Foundation for Culture

TRANSLATION NOTE
This book follows the Hepburn system of romanization of Japanese words. All Japanese names appearing in this book are written in the Western order, with the given name first. All personal titles of the public figures mentioned in this book are as of the publication date of the Japanese edition in 2017.

Lost in Evolution: Exploring Humanity's Path in Asia
Hiroto Kawabata.
Technical advisor: Yousuke Kaifu.
Translator: Dana Lewis.

Published by
Japan Publishing Industry Foundation for Culture (JPIC)
2-2-30 Kanda-Jinbocho, Chiyoda-ku, Tokyo 101-0051, Japan

First English edition: March 2020

Book design: Kazuhiko Miki, Ampersand Works
Front and cover photos: National Museum of Nature and Science, Tokyo

Printed in Japan
ISBN 978-4-86658-133-0
https://japanlibrary.jpic.or.jp/

Introduction

What comes to mind when you think of the people of prehistoric Asia? For me, it used to be Peking Man and Java Man—whom scientists call *Homo erectus*. Java Man in particular, discovered in the late nineteeth century, was a first in anthropological history and was widely acclaimed as the missing link between apes and humans. This link led to his being prominently featured in natural history museums and to widespread recognition of the name.

More than a hundred years after that discovery, it is agreed today that humans emerged first in Africa. As a consequence, anthropological research has focused primarily on Africa, leaving Asia somewhat in the shadows as a relatively neglected area of study. But there have been a number of exciting discoveries in Asia in the last twenty years. One major surprise was the 2003 discovery of a smaller species, Flores Man, nicknamed "hobbit," on Indonesia's Flores Island. There was also the 2010 DNA identification of a new species now known as Denisovans. And there have been more recent discoveries: in 2015 of a distinctly robust jawbone likely from a new species in Taiwan's Penghu Channel and then reports in 2018 of human bones from another new species of ancient humans in the Philippines, from Luzon. All of this clear evidence of human evolution in Asia has sparked renewed interest in Asia as an area once inhabited by many different species.

This book grew out of an effort to gain a better understanding of the peoples who populated Asia in ancient times and to present these findings from a modern *Homo sapiens* perspective. Books on human evolution have long been popular in Japan, and the genre has spawned a number of best sellers. Regrettably, most have been translations of works originally written in English. Even as they dealt with fascinating questions like how humans evolved from their African origins, when *Homo sapiens* came out of Africa, how Neanderthals and *Homo sapiens* coexisted in Europe, when and how the European population transitioned from Neanderthals to *Homo sapiens*, and how *Homo sapiens* spread to Eurasia and then to the Americas, I was left with the mystery of who lived in Asia and when, a question that these popular books seemed to have overlooked. Of course, all authors write with a target audience in mind, and the target audience is an important consideration in deciding what to include in a book. A book written for people living in Europe naturally focuses on the Neanderthals who earlier populated Europe and then the Cro-Magnons who followed them as the first European *Homo sapiens*. Likewise, readers in North America are likely to be interested in the great journey taken by humanity to and then across the Americas; Australian readers curious about where the indigenous people's ancestors came from; and Pacific islanders about how people came to live on this or that island. More broadly speaking, people like me who live in Asia might be expected to want to find out what human species lived in Asia and when.

Since the book I wanted to read didn't exist, I decided to find these things out firsthand. And the best place to start was by talking with Dr. Yousuke Kaifu of Tokyo's National Museum of Nature and Science, who brought me up to date on anthropological research in Asia. The result is this book. Though I originally wrote the book for Japanese readers, my hope is that it will prove a catalyst in conveying a wealth of information not readily available to English-language readers.

Of course, I mainly hope you'll enjoy the quest to unearth the secrets of human evolution in Asia as depicted here. Another hope is that I've shed some light, albeit from a different angle, on the universal questions of where we came from and what the future holds. All of us essentially have our origins in Africa, and this Asian chapter enlarges the ever-evolving story of humankind's great journey from past to present, living in regions far and wide across the planet.

Hiroto Kawabata
December 2019

Contents

CHAPTER 3

Where It Happens: Putting Science to Work on Java Man 63

Grand Entrance from an Island Cave 93

CHAPTER 5

Big News from the Basin

CHAPTER 6

Up from Taiwan's Ocean Floor

Lost in Evolution

Uncovering
Homo erectus
in Asia

Hands in the Dirt

Indonesia's central island of Java. A small community, Sambungmacan, by the banks of the Solo River.

Along these riverbanks is a spot where the surface layer of earth has been carefully cleared away to reveal strata. In the shade of a blue plastic tarp stretched over the site to shield it from the sun is an archaeological dig.

At first glance, the dig seems to be just a section of the bank where the sloping earth has been cleared away and leveled. At the back of this zone, the exposed strata appear as a vertical wall nearly chest high. Two trenches have been cut about a meter deep into the earth in the flat area between the strata and *bengawan* (Indonesian for "river"). These excavation trenches are rectangular, each about two meters wide and three meters long.

A wall. Two trenches. People are stationed at all three, working quietly and steadily, hands in the dirt. This is the prospect at the Sambungmacan excavation site, where on a day in September 2014 I joined my very first dig.

Our work began early, about 8:00 a.m., was it? At first the morning air was quite cool, but within an hour the temperature had soared, and now I was sweating rivers. Every time I paused to swab my face with my towel, I could see the other river. And smell the pungent stench rising off its waters.

Bengawan Solo is a meandering waterway that springs from the earth near the foot of Mt. Lawu, a stratovolcano in Central Java, to wend its way across the island before emptying into the ocean near Surabaya, a port city on the island's east coast. To people living along the shores of Bengawan Solo, it's also a river of life that sustains their livelihoods. September is Indonesia's dry season, and the river waters were low. The current was so feeble, the water so stagnant, that it was hard to tell which way was downstream. Here and there, bubbly white foam marked the river's surface, making it seem anything but hygienic.

On the other hand, so long as you ignored the smell, it was a wonderfully picturesque sight. In that narrow, wriggling water, you could see people in flat-bottom boats plumbing the riverbed with long poles for

Fig. 1: The Solo River flows through Sambungmacan village on Java Island.

sand to use in making concrete. Children played on vacant land along the riverbanks. Everywhere I looked was an image alluring enough to capture for my computer's screensaver.

Our focus at the time, however, was not on the scenery (or hygienic state of the river). Our group of some 30 people, each in our assigned positions, was focused entirely on reading the exposed strata. The team consisted of three Japanese—Dr. Yousuke Kaifu, paleontologist Akio Takahashi, and me—and everyone else was Indonesian. Some were trained excavation experts from the Indonesian Geological Research and Development Centre in Bandung, others were local villagers hired for this project. In fact, this region is one of the most productive places in Java for finding human fossils, with three well-preserved prehistoric skulls discovered in this area—so far.

The sharp ring of metal striking metal echoed across the site. To expose more of the strata, some workers were using chisels and thick spikes to gradually deepen and widen the trenches. Among those team members was a young villager carefully scraping away the earth around an exposed object, long and thin. It turned out to be part of a fossilized water buffalo or other creature, a piece of history buried beneath the surface for hundreds of thousands of years.

Just the sight of such an ancient remain gradually emerging from the soil had the power to stir the heart. The youth worked on, absolutely absorbed, his eyes shining. A little farther away, an old woman with bent back was sifting a scattering of rocks with a testing sieve, removing any that caught her attention and adding them to a prepared container. She handles each stone with as much care as she would a gold nugget. She, too, was completely absorbed.

There's something about this work that bewitches all involved, regardless of age or gender.

"Another Human": So Close, but Different from Us

As for me, there I stood, September 2014, in Sambungmacan at Dr. Kaifu's invitation. I was on my first dig to find early human fossils.

Sambungmacan has yielded a multitude of fossils that washed down Bengawan Solo eons ago and accumulated at the village site. These fossils date back millions of years, to a time after Java was first tectonically uplifted from the ocean floor and became land. From bones of *Stegolophodon trigonocephalus* (an extinct elephant species) to fossils of water buffalo, deer, rhinos, tigers, crocodiles, and enormous giant tortoises, the evolving fauna of the island over changing eras are now coming to light.

And living among these many animals so long ago were "humans," or "hominins" in more academic terms, which includes all humankind that ever lived on this planet. Hominins who lived together with the above extinct animals on Java were different from us, yet nonetheless still much closer to us than chimpanzees and other great apes. They were members of the genus *Homo* that flourished here for countless years.

In Japan, we're used to referring to these early beings as "*Java genjin*," which can be translated as "Javanese *Homo erectus*" academically, or "Java Man" popularly. Their fossils were first discovered in the nineteenth century and were hailed by their discoverers as being the long-sought missing link between today's humans and our great ape ancestors. Even today they remain one of the best-known examples of fossil hominin in the history of paleoanthropology.

Their scientific name is *Homo erectus,* but not that long ago they were more often called *Pithecanthropus erectus. Pithecanthropus* had a meaning close to "apelike man." Nowadays it's considered more accurate to place them in genus *Homo* to emphasize their proximity to modern man. "*Erectus,*" of course, refers to walking upright. They were already living on Java some 1.2 million years ago, and while we still do not know very much about them, it appears they were there as recently as 50,000 years ago.

Fifty-thousand years ago. Consider that. Fifty-thousand years ago, we

Fig. 2: Excavation work at the two trenches.

modern humans, *H. sapiens,* had already appeared in Africa, travelled out of that continent, and reached every corner of Eurasia. Indeed, it's now believed *H. sapiens* had already reached Australia, the last continent we populated, 47,000 years ago. Java Man was also around at that time and had been about three millennia earlier.

Nor were they alone. Hominins other than Java Man who were more primitive than us *Homo sapiens* were also still living in Asia. Neanderthal remains have been found in southern Siberia, and since the turn of the century, we've discovered that some of the same locations that hold Neanderthal fossils also have fossils of another little-known archaic human: the Denisovan. Meanwhile, *H. floresiensis,* known colloquially as hobbit for their size, were living quite close to Java. What's more, the first known archaic *Homo* remains to be found in Taiwan were recently dredged from the ocean floor off the Penghu Islands.

How varied the human landscape must have been in those days! This prehistoric diversity was of an order altogether different from the one we *Homo sapiens* experience today. Seen from a DNA perspective, we're virtually homogenous—in biological terms, a single species. Yet only a short while ago there were multiple, completely different species of humans coexisting on Planet Earth. Far from being unusual, that was the normal state of affairs. Scientists today believe there was once a human diversity that would make our modern heads spin.

Many people today assume the loci of research into the fossil record of humankind are in Africa. They're right—to a degree. Africa has been

Fig. 3: A thick spike is pounded into the earth to reveal the strata.

clearly established as the cradle of humanity, the focus of keen interest today and tomorrow. Yet Asia—once home to so many diverse early humans—was also an evolutionary hotspot. Of all Asia, the island of Java is where we continue to unearth the largest number of fossils of archaic humans. It has become one of the great centers for research into human evolution, and expectations are high it will provide a benchmark for better understanding human diversity.

What kinds of humans were living on that prehistoric Earth? How did they live? In what kinds of environments? And above all, why did they all disappear? Why are we the only ones left? It's no exaggeration to say that research into premodern humans taking place in Asia today holds the key to unlocking these mysteries.

Hotbed of Discovery

Let me sketch out a simple roadmap of the route ahead of us.

First, under Dr. Kaifu's sure tutelage, Chapter 1 will secure a broad understanding of the history of human evolution. Then, with that clear, we'll move on to examine in detail the most archetypal of all Asian archaic hominins: Java Man.

To do this, we'll visit Trinil on Java, the original discovery site, and Sangiran, the most productive Java Man excavation site on the island. Then we'll pause to look into the historical backdrop behind the discovery. The first Java Man fossils were discovered in 1891, during a time when the theory of evolution was finally gaining wide acceptance. It turns out that this "missing link between man and monkey," as Java Man was so often characterized at the time, is now assuming fresh importance in the twenty-first century. What is this new landscape of human history that Java Man is helping configure for us today?

And then, once we've got our feet wet with Java Man, we will move on to consider the relatively new kid on the block, the legendary hobbit, *Homo floresiensis.* The 2004 announcement of the discovery of fossil remains of this tiny primitive human created a worldwide sensation, spurring a lively debate that continues to this day. Consider one of the many burning questions raised about this human: Did *H. floresiensis*—said to have been no more than a meter tall—originally branch off from Java Man before becoming so tiny? Or is it possible that the relatively small, and much more primitive African early *Homo, Homo habilis,* made it out of Africa all the way to today's Indonesian island of Flores, there evolving independently into *H. floresiensis*? For that matter, how is it possible for such small humans to have come into existence?

Dr. Kaifu is a member of the international scientific team studying the hobbit and is responsible for leading research on its skull and teeth. In the pages ahead, he'll give us a glimpse into the nitty-gritty of how science is done on the ground, a process that resembles nothing so much as a detective story.

As if this weren't enough, we'll include a quick word about the Taiwanese archaic *Homo*, officially identified as Penghu 1, whose fossilized jawbone was recently recovered from the seabed near Taiwan, surprising the world's human evolution researchers yet again.

In 2015, two years prior to first publication of our book, this news rocked the anthropology community. Penghu 1 was announced as a previously unrecognized form of archaic Asian hominin, reinforcing the impression that the world of early humans in Asia was a region of great diversity—as Africa's is known to have been—with multiple species existing in close proximity during the same periods of time. Dr. Kaifu was a member of the team that identified Penghu 1, and with the tale of this discovery, I hope to convey the processes involved in the discovery of a new human and the great excitement surrounding it.

Heading Out

Now that we've set our course, let's head out. By following the route laid out above, we'll go on to meet those close, close neighbors we've never met owing to a difference of some tens and hundreds of thousands of years. This is what's possible when we draw on the power of science.

Once we've done all this, I hope that together we may finally close in on an answer to that deep, primal doubt I myself have harbored for so long: Why are we *Homo sapiens* the only human species left in our world today?

Fig. 4: Dr. Kaifu organizes animal fossils from a dig.

CHAPTER 1

Overview of Human Evolution

The Five Grades

The National Museum of Nature and Science research departments and Collection Center are in Tsukuba Science City, Ibaraki Prefecture, northern part of Tokyo. As such, the Tsukuba Research Facility curates more than 4.6 million natural history specimens and is Japan's largest center for the preservation and study of such specimens.

Sitting in a corner of his Tsukuba office, surrounded by replicas of early human specimens, Dr. Kaifu crossed his arms in thought.

"And so. Where to begin?"

This was his first response to my vague declaration that I wanted him to tell me everything about archaic humans and human evolution in Asia.

"When we talk about humanity," he continued, "you first must understand we're talking about seven million years of history. In very broad strokes, think of humankind as having evolved through five distinct grades: pre-australopiths, australopiths, early *Homo*, late archaic *Homo*, and modern humans."

My first question had already produced five new terms:

pre-australopiths and **australopiths**, creatures who were still very much like the apes but had moved into our ancient family line;

early *Homo*, the first members of genus *Homo,* the starting point leading to today's human beings;

late archaic *Homo*, an older cohort than we are but still much closer to us than previous grades; and lastly,

modern humans—in other words, us.

A lot of terms, true, but not so hard to remember. The key thing to remember about these five grades is that human beings evolved into who we are today by passing through each grade along the way. These five grades are traditionally used in Japan to describe the broad outline of human evolution to general audiences without getting into confusing and controversial scientific nomenclature. Early *Homo*, whom we'll discuss in detail later in the book, represent just one of the steps along the path to today's modern humans.

It is impossible to properly understand the significance of those early *Homo* in isolation. We first must arm ourselves with a broad understanding of all seven million years of human evolution. When you start examining the history of humankind at the granular level, you quickly discover there are countless disputes and debates surrounding it, as well as a host of questions that are unanswered to this day. Since this is a book for non-specialists like myself, let's skip those knotty particulars and just invite Dr. Kaifu to describe in very broad strokes the current established theory regarding the evolution of our species—thinking already strongly supported by extensive evidence.

Pre-australopiths: Semi-Arboreal & Semi-Terrestrial

"The group I refer to as pre-australopiths lived on the African continent some 7 to 4.4 million years ago," Dr. Kaifu said. "They're thought to have lived a life that was part arboreal and part terrestrial. The very oldest pre-australopiths we presently know of is genus *Sahelanthropus*, whom we know from fossils first discovered in Chad. *Sahelanthropus* is believed to have lived there approximately seven to six million years ago. Most of the fossils found so far have been crania and mandibles. I sometimes like to place a cast of a *Sahelanthropus* skull in a line with casts of various ape skulls and have my students try to identify the differences for practice.

"Here in Japan, however," Dr. Kaifu continued, "*Ardipithecus ramidus,* another pre-australopith species that lived about 4.4 million years ago, is better known than *Sahelanthropus.* One reason is that many more specimens have been found for *Ardipithecus* than for *Sahelanthropus.* Another reason is that *Ardipithecus* was discovered by Dr. Gen Suwa of the University of Tokyo, who discovered the first piece of *Ardipithecus* fossils while working at a site in the Afar Rift region of Ethiopia, so the Japanese press always pays special attention to any news about *Ardipithecus.*"
A little background informa-

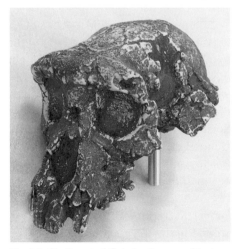

Fig. 1-1: Skull cast of *Sahelanthropus*, oldest known hominin.

tion might be in order. It's thought that a key indicator of the point where progenitors of humankind branched off from other primates to follow a unique evolutionary path is the adoption of a terrestrial mode of life in preference to the previous arboreal primate lifestyle. Along the way, it is theorized, there first would have been what Dr. Kaifu refers to as "pre-austra-lopiths" beings who spent part of their lives in the trees but lived the greater part on the ground.

When I visited Dr. Kaifu at his Tsukuba office, he had a cast of a seven-million-year-old *Sahelanthro-pus* skull sitting on his desk. This particular fossil was what is called

Fig. 1-2: A skull cast of *Ardipithecus ramidus* in the Royal Tyrrell Museum, Canada.

a "holotype," that is, a specimen used by scientists for defining the charac-teristics of a genus and species (in this case, *Sahelanthropus tchadensis*). The skull was plopped down there so casually that I had no idea it was a replica of such a rare fossil.

In contrast to the partial remains of *Sahelanthropus* that have been found to date, enough specimens of *Ardipithecus ramidus* have been unearthed to allow scientists to reconstruct an almost complete skeleton. Papers on this and other aspects of *A. ramidus* research were published in *Science* (October 2009), enabling us to visualize what kind of pre-australopiths they were. A popular attraction at the National Museum of Nature and Science (hereafter, National Museum) exhibition facilities in Tokyo's Ueno Park is Theater 36○, a spherical video theater where projected images surround the audience. One of the program titles is *The Jour-ney of Humans,* a film produced under Dr. Kaifu's direction. The movie begins with a party of *A. ramidus* making a computer graphic appearance. Depicted *Ardipithecus* are basically forest dwellers who sometimes climb around in the trees but at other times descend to the ground, where they walk bipedally. The film also portrays them as omnivores, consuming plants and small animals.

The key point is that *Ardipithecus ramidus*, an early species of pre-austr-alopiths, represents a grade when the progenitors of today's humankind were still adapting from life in the forests to life on the veldt. It truly was a transitional period, when adaptation to bipedal walking was not yet complete.

Interestingly, *A. ramidus* had a cranial capacity of only approximately 300 cc, about the same as that of modern primates like today's chimpanzees and bonobos. They're believed to have been small, too, only about 120 cm tall. I mention this because, as we go forward, we'll find these three elements—bipedalism, cranial capacity, and body size—are considered critical parameters in the scientific study of human evolution.

Upright Walkers: The Australopiths

"Next," continued Dr. Kaifu, "we come to the group I refer to as australopiths. Their terrestrial aspects were much more pronounced than the pre-australopiths' were, and they habitually walked upright (erect). There were various kinds of australopiths living at different times and in different locations, but their distribution stayed limited to the African continent. The earliest of these, whom scientists call *Australopithecus*, appeared around 4.2 million years ago, and a second branch split off about 2.7 million years ago that we identify today as *Paranthropus*.

Australopithecus was a comparatively gracile (or small and slender) australopith and, also appearing in Japanese history textbooks, it ranks up there with Java Man *(H. erectus)* as one of the best-known human ancestors among Japanese.

A full-size representation of the famous *Australopithecus afarensis* individual popularly known as Lucy is on display at the National Museum with a cast of her skeleton by her side. Dr. Hisao Baba, a former head of the museum's Department of Anthropology and the man who pointed Dr. Kaifu in the direction of researching Java Man, supervised this exhibit's creation. His concept for the reconstructed Lucy was that she be shown as having been "suddenly transported into the future, and being astonished by what she sees." I personally find the museum's Lucy both innocent and strangely charming. Lucy was only about 110 cm tall and had a cranial capacity of some 400 cc.

In contrast to the skulls of *Australopithecus*, those of *Paranthropus* have boney sagittal crests, faces that spread out wide to the sides, and other features that give them a unique appearance. These distinctive

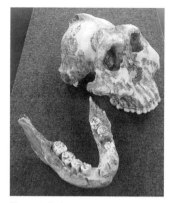

Fig. 1-3: Lucy represented (left) and (right) with a cast of her skeleton.

Fig. 1-4: Robust australopith skull and jawbone.

characteristics suggest they were highly specialized; yet as a group they appear to have existed far longer than did the other, more normal-appearing *Australopithecus*. Their unusual features must have offered them a powerful adaptive advantage.

The Big-Brained "Early *Homo*": *Homo habilis*

"Between three and two million years ago, early *Homo* appear, again in Africa," stated Dr. Kaifu. "*Homo habilis* was one of the earliest, and they clearly had larger brains than australopiths, as well as smaller jaws and teeth. They relied heavily on stone tools and frequently ate meat. All these things set them apart, both culturally and behaviorally, from australopiths."

At last, we have the debut of the genus *Homo*: *H. habilis* appears to have been the earliest, or one of the earliest, of them.

By this point there must be a number of readers who are saying to themselves, "Hey, now I understand. When naming living things in an academic setting, it is standard to use binomial nomenclature, the so-called 'two-term naming system.'" For those not familiar with this topic, let me quickly explain. Binomial nomenclature is a naming system for living creatures where the subject is listed not only by the name of the specific species to which it belongs but also by the name of the higher genus to which that species belongs.

For example, in the case of Lucy, she has been identified by scientists as an *Australopithecus afarensis,* where *Australopithecus* is her genus name and *afarensis* her species name. Or, to take another example: in the case of the pre-australopith *Ardipithecus ramidus, Ardipithecus* would be the genus name and *ramidus* the species name.

Likewise, in our earlier examination of pre-australopiths and australopiths, we discussed genus *Ardipithecus* and genus *Australopithecus.* When we discuss *Homo habilis,* the genus name has changed to *Homo.* This is a critical point. The genus name *Homo,* as you can see, is the very same genus name attached to us humans alive today, *Homo sapiens.*

"Many things are still unknown about the origin of the genus *Homo,*" observes Dr. Kaifu. "Yet everyone in the field recognizes *Homo habilis* as one of the earliest *Homo* to have appeared. We observe little change among early hominins in cranial capacity from the pre-australopiths on through to australopiths. Yet once the early *Homo, Homo habilis,* appears, brain size begins to increase dramatically with every subsequent species until we reach us modern humans. At the same time, we observe that the masticatory apparatus—teeth and jaw—gets smaller as humankind evolves."

When you examine a *Homo habilis* fossil, you find the size of the cranial cavity averages only a little over 600 cc. Even the largest skulls found to date don't exceed 800 cc in capacity, and their bodies were not particularly large, either.

From that point on, however, the expansion of the brain is astounding. Fig. 1-5 shows the incredible growth in brain size for humankind since *Homo habilis.*

In contrast to pre-australopiths and australopiths, where cranial capacity increased only marginally over millions and millions of years, we can see from the graph that brain size began to soar beginning from the time of *H. habilis* some two million years ago.

Nor was that the only change. We can see early *Homo* after *Homo habilis* becoming steadily more modern across other indices as well. Body size surges, and there's also an even more dramatic shrinkage of the teeth and jaw.

Think about this point the next time you go to the zoo. Take a moment to compare the profile of your own face or that of your companions with the profiles of the primates there. You'll note the primate face slants outward from the forehead to the jaw, and the jaw protrudes. Modern human jawbones, by contrast, are now very small—so small we appear flat-faced,

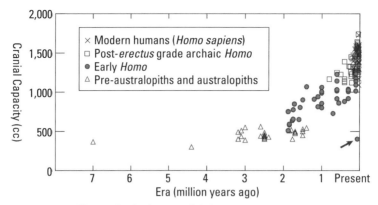

Fig. 1-5: Brain size growth in human evolution.
Arrow indicates *Homo floresiensis,* from Chapter 4.

with our profile dropping perpendicularly from our forehead straight down to our jawbone. Take a look in the mirror to see what I mean.

Another revelation to come was clear evidence that *H. habilis* was a prodigious user of stone tools in daily life. Indeed, the Latin *Homo habilis* means "skilled, clever person." In all kinds of ways, *Homo habilis* took the first steps down the path leading to us humans here today. From that point on, the pace of human evolution really took off.

First to Leave Africa: *Homo erectus*

In contrast to the earliest *Homo, Homo habilis,* who in the end stayed put in Africa, there was an early *Homo* species who became the first to make the leap from the continent of its origin to Eurasia, becoming the very first members of the genus *Homo* to migrate from Africa. We call them *Homo erectus.*

H. erectus fossils have been found not only in Africa but across a vast territory beyond. The species travelled far across Asia. We know them today as Peking Man in northeast Asia and as Java Man on Java island in Southeast Asia. They were a durable species that existed for well over a million years.

"The size of the *Homo erectus* brain grew steadily over time until it was nearly two-thirds the size of modern man's," observed Dr. Kaifu. "Their bodies were large and their legs long, which made them very efficient bipedal walkers. As a consequence, their habitat expanded enormously. It's what enabled them to become the first to leave the African continent and eventually travel as far as the eastern shores of Eurasia."

Without question, the example of *H. erectus* for which the most fossils have been found—and whose evolutionary history we can track in the greatest detail over the longest period of time—is Java Man. By the end of Java Man's time on Earth, their cranial capacity had reached 1,200 cc, just a hair's breadth under the average 1,400 cc of your average *H. sapiens*.

Homo erectus were also quite tall. Some are thought to have reached adult heights of as much as 160 to more than 180 cm. You'll also find a *Homo erectus* skeleton cast and lifelike representation on display at the National Museum. However, this individual is not Java Man but someone known as Turkana Boy: a young male alive some

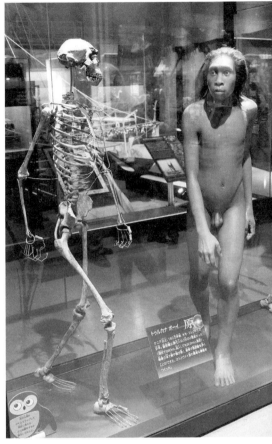

Fig. 1-6: *Homo erectus* youth known as Turkana Boy.

1.5 million years ago whose fossilized remains were discovered at an excavation site along the shores of Lake Turkana in Kenya.

Turkana Boy is believed to have died around age 11, based on extrapolations from modern human standards. The museum model was created and posed on the premise that, like Lucy, he has been transported to the present day. Though certainly startled by such time travel, Turkana Boy, like any other young man, is trying his best not to show it. It's surprising to learn this ancient youth was already 165 cm tall when he died. Had he been a modern human, he'd have been a remarkably tall 11-year-old.

I should also mention, before we move on, there is a school of thought maintaining that the fossils of early *H. erectus* found in East Africa are not from *H. erectus* at all but from a different species, which should properly be named *Homo ergaster* ("working person"). Should you find yourself at the National Museum, you'll see the display signage lists both names.

Brains as Big as Our Own: Late Archaic *Homo*

Next is the coming of late archaic *Homo*.

"Beginning between 1,000,000 and 600,000 years ago in Africa, around 600,000 years ago in Europe, and some 300,000 years ago in Asia, late archaic *Homo* appear with brains even larger than *Homo erectus* and with several other characteristics very close to those of modern humans," states Dr. Kaifu. "Many scientists believe they first evolved in Africa from *Homo erectus* and then travelled out of Africa to Eurasia. The most famous of them is Neanderthal, or *Homo neanderthalensis,* widely distributed across today's Europe from about 300,000 years ago to as recently as only 40,000 years ago."

Neanderthal is another superstar among our human ancestors whom most people already know from school textbooks. In recent years it's become possible to extract viable fragments of DNA from some Neanderthal fossils, resulting in a rush of exciting new genetic discoveries. Making headlines around the world was an analysis of these DNA snippets which proved conclusively that Neanderthals had crossbred with modern *Homo sapiens.*

Yet there's more the ancient DNA has to tell us. DNA studies of fossils from a cave near southern Siberia's Altai Mountains suggest those people were not Neanderthals, as originally believed, but another archaic *Homo* group now known as Denisovan. Indeed, DNA analysis suggests Denisovans may have interbred with *Homo sapiens* and traces of their DNA can still be found in Melanesians and other populations today.

At the very end of our journey, Denisovans will make another appearance, confronting us with a truly great mystery, so please remember that name.

Fossils have also been found in China—in strata more recent than those yielding the famous *H. erectus* Peking Man—that appear to come from yet another more advanced archaic *Homo*. Mysteries still abound about the nature of late archaic *Homo*. For example, as of this writing, it's unknown whether all archaic *Homo* found in Europe, Asia, and elsewhere shared a common African ancestor.

 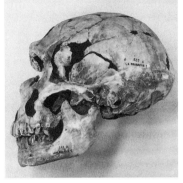

Fig. 1-7: A diorama imagining life among the Neanderthals in the Neanderthal Museum, Germany.

Fig. 1-8: *Homo neanderthalensis* skull.

Setting such concerns aside for the moment, one thing we do know with confidence is that the debut of late archaic *Homo* takes our discussion into a different dimension. Unlike their much earlier predecessors, some of them had brains as large as or larger than those of modern humans. Neanderthal skulls have been found with cranial cavities exceeding 1,600 cc! It's clear that, with the arrival of Neanderthals and the other late archaic *Homo*, we are finally on the verge of the rise of modern humans.

Modern Humans: *Homo sapiens* and the End of Diversity

Unlike the names we've used for the other four grades, "modern humans" refers to one species only: *Homo sapiens.* It means, in the most narrowly defined sense of the word, "us" and no one else.

Those people, sometimes referred to as Cro-Magnon in Europe—and called *"Jomonjin"* (Jomon people) in Japan—are all the same people: *Homo sapiens,* our direct ancestors and the same species as all humans living today.

All primitive populations that we've looked at so far—pre-australopiths, australopiths, early *Homo*, or even late archaic *Homo*—were diverse. In every age prior to our own, there were highly varied species living across the planet at the same time. Yet when we reach the age of *Homo sapiens,* for some reason that regional diversity of humanity has been lost.

"According to present theory, the origin of today's humans, everywhere in the world, traces back ultimately to Africa some 300,000 to 100,000 years ago, to the common ancestor of all modern humans," explains Dr. Kaifu as we sit in his office in Tsukuba. "All kinds of evidence, and particularly findings from morphology and genetic anthropology, come together to support that opinion. Mankind evolved from archaic *Homo* in Africa, and then, sometime after, left Africa to scatter across the entire planet, resulting in today's populations of modern humans in every corner of the world."

The sequence of events Dr. Kaifu describes here is the Out-of-Africa Theory regarding the birth and spread of *Homo sapiens*. This theory is surprisingly recent, having only become solidly established in the twenty-first century. In the past there was considerable support for an alternative, the Multiregional Hypothesis, which proposes that archaic groups of *Homo* evolved into modern humans in multiple regions of the world.

The balance of the debate shifted decisively, from the late 1980s onward, as techniques for dating fossils improved and new technology became available for examining the issue at the genetic level. Add to that the repeated discoveries of new fossil evidence in Africa and a wave of reports of archaeological evidence, and the Out-of-Africa Theory has now become nearly unshakeable. Many more general books have been written about the drama of humankind's emergence from Africa, and I encourage all readers whose interest has been stirred by this short discussion to read them.

"What I find profoundly interesting," muses Dr. Kaifu, "is that at the point in time when *Homo sapiens* actually does leave Africa, what we call humankind was still extremely diverse. Neanderthals and other archaic *Homo* were established across Eurasia, and there were still populations of *Homo erectus* living in Southeast Asia."

His words send a shock wave through me.

Just a few pages back, I wrote that, with the arrival of *Homo sapiens,* humanity's regional diversity disappeared. Yet here is Dr. Kaifu telling me that, even after we *Homo sapiens* made our first appearance—even after those days when we left Africa to spread out around the planet— *Homo erectus* and other archaic forms of *Homo* still lived on and the diversity of the genus *Homo* was extremely rich. Yet now, at this very moment, when referring to "us humans," we mean only *Homo sapiens*. No one else. Apparently once humankind as we know it today began its march across the planet, all our previously vast diversity disappeared.

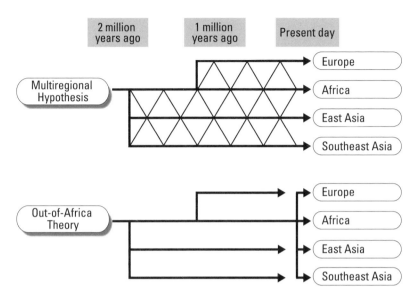

Fig.1-9: Multiregional Hypothesis vs. Out-of-Africa Theory.

Multiregional Hypothesis: *Homo erectus* and more advanced forms of archaic *Homo* in different places around the world evolved and interbred with neighboring populations, resulting in the independent emergence of *Homo sapiens* in multiple locations around the world.

Out-of-Africa Theory: The origin of all modern humans throughout the world traces back to the first appearance of *Homo sapiens* in Africa approximately 200,000 years ago, and *Homo sapiens* subsequently expanded from Africa to the world.

Human Evolution and Geographic Distribution

Up to this point, we've been taking a broad, bird's-eye view of the seven-million-year history of humankind, from ancient pre-australopiths to human beings as we know them today. Let's pause, step back a little, and reexamine that story. This time, however, I'd like to talk about geographical dispersion. How far and wide was humanity distributed across the planet at the different grades in our evolution? This question is quite profound, for geographical distribution and human evolution are quite closely related.

Our early incarnations, pre-australopiths and australopiths, stayed in Africa. *Homo erectus,* however, spread across the whole of Africa and succeeded in leaving the continent itself. *H. erectus* were true pioneers who walked across Asia, the vast continent which in those long-ago days truly was a land "untrodden by the foot of Man," all the way to the eastern edge of Asia. Yet their distribution in Eurasia was limited only to the continent's southern half. The point that marks their northernmost expansion was in today's China, home of the famous Peking Man.

Archaic forms of *Homo* who followed *Homo erectus* extended the territory of humankind in Europe and Asia somewhat farther north. Yet it seems even they were unable to penetrate to the center of frigid Siberia. And then, when at long last *H. sapiens,* we modern humans, emerged from Africa, we spread to every last corner of Eurasia including Siberia. Just tracing on a map the way *H. sapiens* marched on to populate all of North and South America and reach even the islands of the Pacific Ocean, you're bound to be struck by the grandeur of that sweeping drama.

Reading the Human Evolution Story in Our Family Tree

Next, I'd like to consider the phylogenetic relationships of the many varied humans we've met so far. The consensus among researchers today is that humankind didn't evolve in a straight line from pre-australopiths and australopiths, our earliest predecessors, to early and late forms of archaic *Homo*, and lastly to us *Homo sapiens*. Such theories existed in the past, but new advances in research have revealed our evolution was far from simple.

On the detailed family tree Dr. Kaifu created in 2010 for the Human Evolution exhibit at the National Museum, you'll find a point right at the bottom, some seven million years in the past, where the main trunk of the tree continues straight, while another branch veers away in the direction of the chimpanzees, bonobos, and other apes. This point on the chart marks the birth of humankind.

From the tentative label of "earliest hominins?" to "early *Homo*?" and on to the first appearance of *Australopithecus* and other gracile australopiths, the human family tree is one long, continuous trunk. It is possible, however, there were other branches along the way that we don't yet know about. For example, as of this writing, there have been reports of evidence that a population which may have been descendants of *Ardipithecus ramidus*—one of the earliest hominins quite famous in Japan—may have still been living in Africa just some 3.5 million years ago, at a time

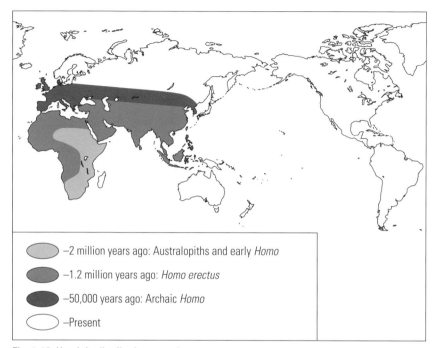

-2 million years ago: Australopiths and early *Homo*

-1.2 million years ago: *Homo erectus*

-50,000 years ago: Archaic *Homo*

-Present

Fig. 1-10: Hominin distribution over time.

when the much later *Australopithecus afarensis* had already become well established.

In fact, the history of the evolution of early hominins beyond this point is extremely complex, and there is much debate among experts. However, a broad consensus has now emerged that the robust forms of australopiths diverged from the line that led to the genus *Homo*.

I should also point out that even the appearance in Africa of *H. habilis* and *H. erectus*—those earliest members of genus *Homo*—did not signal the disappearance of australopiths. The robust australopiths, *Paranthropus*, for example, coexisted with early *Homo* on the African continent for more than a million years after the latter appeared.

Just looking at the almost bizarrely shaped skulls and other fossil remains of *Paranthropus*, they seem to have been an extremely specialized form of primitive humankind. Despite this—or perhaps because of

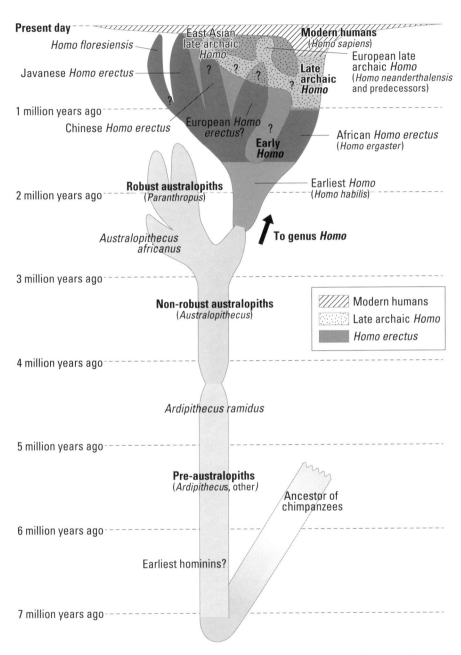

Fig. 1-11: Hominin family tree (based on dominant hypotheses as of March 2010).

this—it appears they segregated themselves from the genus *Homo* and continued to flourish parallel to them for an extremely long time.

Meanwhile, we see on the family tree that the line of early *Homo* itself soon begins to branch, and to branch again. *Homo erectus,* after becoming the first of our distant ancestors to leave Africa, separates out into regional clusters like Java Man and Peking Man, while those *H. erectus* who stayed in Africa emerge as the African late archaic *Homo. Homo neanderthalensis* and other similar forms split off from this group and go their own away until finally the African archaic *Homo* give rise to yet another line, those humans we know best today, *Homo sapiens.* This is the scenario of human evolution that can be read from our family tree.

There still are some particularly troublesome questions regarding that very last group to come before us. If we turn our attention to Europe, for example, we find it still difficult to grasp the relationship between the first hominins who appeared in that region and the Neanderthals who followed. Likewise, there is disagreement as to whether late archaic *Homo* from China evolved there *in situ* from Peking Man, *Homo erectus pekinensis,* or if they arrived there from elsewhere in Eurasia. That's why you'll find lots of question marks on the family tree, each an issue needing to be explicated and proven.

That concludes our crash course on the basics of the history of humankind. And with that, we have our bag of tools loaded and are ready to go. So let's step into the world of research into *Homo erectus* and other archaic *Homo* of Asia, that field of study which is the center of such hot debate today.

CHAPTER 2

The Java Story

Sentimental Journey to See an Old Friend

Back when I was in junior high or high school, Java Man appeared in our textbooks and reference books under the scientific classification *Pithecanthropus.* He was also referred to as *chokuritsu genjin,* a Japanese term that translates as "upright standing early hominin."

Both the Latin and the Japanese names evoked images that struck me deeply then: *Pi-the-can-thro-pus,* a long, mysterious tongue twister; upright standing early hominin. They swept me into another realm of thought: Who on earth could this upright standing early hominin be? Even now I'm surprised by people's responses when I ask if they've heard of *Pithecanthropus,* or Java Man, or upright standing early hominin: almost everyone instantly replies in the affirmative.

Many things I learned in junior high would have a powerful impact on my life, but *Pithecanthropus*—the enigmatic upright standing early hominin—is one of the most significant. Although the name burrowed into my mind, I can't recall when I first heard it. Was it in the history portion of our social studies curriculum? Or part of earth science in our science curriculum? Or was it in biology? It seemed to occupy a mysterious space between science and social studies but could easily have been both.

In writing this book, I've found out that the *Pithecanthropus* was taught in my world history class. I also encountered *Pithecanthropus* in my high school biology class—this time described as the so-called "missing link" between primates and us modern humans. So I can only conclude that my memory is jumbled because I encountered the subject in many different contexts.

When you think about it, the reason for the multiple contexts is simple: *Pithecanthropus* or *Homo erectus*, as we'll be saying throughout the book, is intimately linked to our origin. That link also appears in those deep, universal questions of fundamental interest long before knowledge got divided into different disciplines, namely: "Where did we come from, and where are we bound?" No matter where we were, no matter what the era, we humans have sought those answers in ways reflecting the knowledge and intellectual tools available at the time and place. Sometimes the answer has taken the form of mythology, at other times philosophy or history.

Now the discipline at the center of scientific inquiry into where we come from is anthropology. Yet given that any inquiry at the cutting edge of science often transcends disciplines, it may not be meaningful to ask whether our pursuit is in the province of history, biology, or earth science. We should forget the pigeonholes and be prepared to use all the tools at our disposal.

It turns out that my initial exposure to the *Pithecanthropus* name bumped me into a realm of inquiry we humans have been exploring since time immemorial, one beyond the framework of school study, with a power sufficient enough to have driven a wedge into the relentless rhythm of my daily life. Ever since that first encounter, be it how many decades ago, whenever I look back over my path, that wedge is still pounded into place as it always has been, reminding me that *Pithecanthropus* = Java Man.

That is why for me, and I suspect for many readers, my sojourn in pursuit of Java Man is a kind of sentimental journey. You might even say it's something of a pilgrimage. When I traveled to Java at Dr. Kaifu's invitation, I had an opportunity to visit Trinil, the site where the first Java Man fossils were discovered. I was staying in the city of Sragen, at a location which not only had easy access to many excavation sites along the Solo River that yielded Java Man fossils but was also very close to Sambungmacan, Dr. Kaifu's current excavation site. I decided to take half a day off from the dig and see the remains of the Trinil excavation. During our drive there, I felt bittersweet excitation.

P.e. 175M ONO 1891/93

After turning off the main highway and driving along a winding side road, we came out on a riverside terrace overlooking the Solo River. This is where you meet the elephant. Not a living elephant, but one made of concrete. Its tusks are extremely long, and the figure is clearly different from Asian and African elephants. It replicates an extinct elephant, Stegodon, a prehistoric Asian elephant. I was a bit shocked at how casual the modeling was.

After continuing past the Stegodon and skirting some buildings, I caught sight of the river. Unlike the low riverbank at Sambungmacan where our dig was taking place, the riverbank in Trinil cut steeply away. Looking over the edge at the water below revealed the bank was more like a cliff. Close to the edge is a stone monument: the Trinil Stone. The first thing I noticed was "P.e." in large letters: *Pithecanthropus erectus*.

Below P.e. is an arrow and the legend: 175M ONO. "ONO" is the abbreviation for *Ostnordost*, German for east-northeast. This meant that the spot where *P. erectus* had been discovered was 175 meters east-northeast from where we were standing. The legend continued: 1891/93. These are the years of the excavation. The man who erected this monument was Eugène Dubois, the Dutch military doctor who discovered Java Man.

Fig. 2-1: A Stegodon statue welcoming me to Trinil.

I stood on the edge of the cutaway bank and squinted east-northeast to a point I guesstimated was 175 meters away. There was a bend in the river, and I could make out an unnatural geometrical pattern that appeared to be oblong ridges, like raised paths between rice paddies in Japan. The zones enclosed by these ridges were flooded with water.

This was the former excavation site described on the Trinil stone. The site is now completely submerged during Java's rainy season, but I was visiting in the dry season, that is, the excavation season. It was September, and the date that Dubois discovered the first fossilized skull of Java Man, as memorialized on his monument, is October 1, 1891. This is the best time of year for digs along the banks of the Solo River. I was astonished by the size of the old excavation site, and its many zones were impressive. The total area excavated exceeded 2,300 square meters (2,400 square meters, including trenches on the opposite bank).

Fig. 2-2: Trinil Stone monument, with "P.e." for *Pithecanthropus erectus*. Dr. Fachroel Aziz of Indonesia's Geological Research and Development Centre was my gracious host.

Two engineers from the Royal Netherlands East Indies Army plus dozens of Indonesian workers labored here for 49 months

Fig. 2-3: Eugène Dubois, discoverer of the first Java Man fossils.

Fig. 2-4: The original
Dubois excavation site.

over the course of 10 years. By historical standards, it was an exceptionally large dig for human fossils. The Netherlands exercised colonial control over Indonesia for more than 300 years and had almost all of Indonesia in its possession from the late nineteeth to the early twentieth century. It is striking that so many resources were assigned to this search for humanity's missing link. While it may not have counted for much compared to the total Netherlands colonial enterprise budget, the search was still a significant expenditure of time, money, and manpower—indicating how intense the interest in humankind's origins was back then.

The *Pithecanthropus* Prophecies

Let's look at the historical background of this discovery in the context of the European milieu. Eugène Dubois (1858–1940) was a Dutch anatomist and geologist. Today we'd call him a paleoanthropologist, as some references do. Until he came along, the discipline didn't exist, because no ancient human fossils had been found that differed from us modern humans, the sole exception being those of European Neanderthals. So when Dubois travelled to the Dutch East Indies (as Indonesia was called under Dutch colonial rule), he did so not as a paleoanthropologist—or even as a practicing fossilologist—but as a military doctor.

In 1886, before his departure for the Dutch East Indies, Dubois taught anatomy at the University of Amsterdam, where he researched comparative anatomy of vertebrate larynxes. Through that research, he developed an interest in human evolution. Dubois was a one-year-old when Charles Darwin published *On the Origin of Species* in 1859, introducing the world to a theory of evolution based on natural selection. As a university lecturer, Dubois was increasingly drawn to Darwin's theory and dreamed of finding the transitional fossil (a.k.a the missing link) between human beings and apes.

The phrase "missing link" refers to the proposition in Darwinian evolution—a continuous and incremental linear process—that the differences between today's human beings and apes are so vast there must have been an intermediate creature or creatures linking the two. Paleoanthropologists just had to find their fossils. "Missing link" is still used colloquially, if infrequently, for this now vanished intermediary.

In fact, some thirty years before Dubois developed his interest in human evolution, Neanderthal fossils had been discovered in 1856, in a cave in Germany's Neander Valley (Neandertal, in German). However, it seems that scientists then had not grasped the import of this discovery. In 1868, the famous German comparative anatomist and avid promoter of Darwin's evolution theory, Ernst Haeckel, had gone so far as to pre-emptively christen the missing link he predicted would be discovered *Pithecanthropus* (Latin, *pithecus,* "ape," and *anthropus,* "human"), and he named it *Pithecanthropus alalus* ("ape man without speech").

Dubois hoped to be the one to discover this missing link, and in 1887 he set his sights on the Dutch East Indies as the place to go. He believed the tropics—home to so many apes closest to humans among the primates—would be an ideal candidate for the birthplace of ancient humans. Much of the Dutch East Indies was tropical rainforest, prime habitat for simians like gibbons and orangutans. He first took a posting on Sumatra, land of the orangutans, but was unable to uncover any early human fossils there. He then secured a transfer to Java. Asking around, he narrowed down the locations that sounded promising for finding fossils. One was Trinil.

He began his excavation at Trinil in August 1891 and soon found many mammal fossils. Among them was a primate molar that would later be identified as having come from *Pithecanthropus erectus,* as Dubois was calling his anticipated transitional fossil. In October he found a skull, and the following year, in 1892, he discovered a thigh bone with a shape suggesting bipedal locomotion.

Convinced he had indeed found the long-sought "missing link," Dubois published a scientific paper in German in 1894 about his findings with a title possibly referencing Haeckel: *Pithecanthropus erectus, eine men-schenaehnliche Uebergangsform aus Java*, which would translate into English as "Pithecanthropus erectus, a human-like transitional form from Java."

Dubois's find is today's *Homo erectus,* and the fossil he described is still used as the reference specimen (the holotype) for identifying the species. *H. erectus* had an extremely broad geographical distribution. Fossils have been found in other parts of Asia, including *H. erectus pekinensis,* aka Peking Man. Yet that first specimen found by Dubois is the holotype for all others.

As for Dubois, he returned to the Netherlands in 1895, where he was granted a position at the University of Amsterdam. While you might think his discoveries in Trinil would have catapulted him into fame, the rest of his story is not so neatly concluded. The specimen Dubois took back from Java became the center of serious argument over whether it was a transitional fossil or not. There was no end to skeptics saying it was the skull of an enormous gibbon or a modern human. In the end, Dubois simply turned his back on the world and for years refused to show his specimen to anyone. It was not until 1923 that he showed the specimen again.

Between the end of the nineteeth and the start of the twentieth century, Darwin's theory of evolution faced intense opposition. It did, after all, directly concern our ancestors and challenged the very identity of humankind. And it was sure to fuel debate between theologians and scientists. The years passed, and in the late 1920s Peking Man fossils were discovered in China, followed in the 1930s by many additional Java Man fossils found in other parts of Java, especially in Sangiran, which is today a World Heritage site: the Sangiran Early Man Site. Dubois' discovery eventually became historical fact, recorded in world history textbooks. Despite his vindication, however, it is recorded that Dubois lived out his later years quietly, for the most part avoiding contact with other people.

Inspired by his work, German zoologist Margarethe Lenore Selenka led another extensive excavation to search for early human fossils at Trinil from 1906 to 1908,

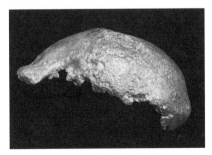

Fig. 2-5. Java Man skull fossil discovered at Trinil.

only to come back empty-handed. In the end, the only human fossils uncovered at Trinil were those first finds by Dubois at the end of the nineteenth century. Today the site of his excavation is mostly underwater, even during Java's dry season: it's sinking slowly into the landscape of the Solo River as boats ply the waters back and forth, in front of the site, collecting sand. After Dubois, the main site for discovery and research on Java shifted to other locations. Yet the historical import of Trinil as the site of the first discovery of Java Man fossils will never change.

Java Man Pilgrimage: Four "Holy" Sites and Sangiran

People unacquainted with Java geography may still know the island is home to the country's capital, Jakarta, and farther east to Surabaya, a city that appears in a popular song by Japanese singer-songwriter Yumi Matsutoya, *Surabaya dori no imoto e* ("To my little sister on Surabaya Street"). You may also know of the island's ancient capitals of Yogyakarta and Surakarta, today known familiarly as Jogja and Solo, respectively.

However, in the coming pages you'll encounter a variety of local place names, so let's pause here to get our bearings. First, a little geologic and geographic background. Java is believed to have been uplifted from the sea some two million years ago, part of the Greater Sunda Islands, with Sumatra to the west and Bali to the east. It is longer east-west than north-south with a surface area of 130,000 square kilometers, about a third the size of the Japanese archipelago, with a population the size of Japan's.

Looking at the map of Java, we see Jakarta on the western edge, and east of it Bandung, a university town replete with research institutes. The Indonesian specialists on the excavation team we'll be visiting are from one such institute, Indonesia's Geological Research and Development Centre. Sites producing the most fossil evidence of Java Man are east of Jakarta or Bandung, far away in the Solo River basin.

Let's zoom in on Fig. 2-7. You see that the Solo River (Bengawan Solo, you'll recall) springs from the western flanks of the stratovolcano, Mt. Lawu. It traces a large circle around Lawu until it changes direction and flows east-west, and from there it meanders on its wriggling way to the east. Some of you will remember the hit Indonesian song *Bengawan Solo* and some may know the movie of the same name by the Japanese film director Kon Ichikawa. Tens of millions of people now live in the

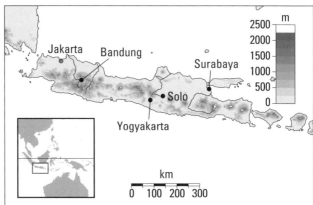

Fig. 2-6: Map of Java.

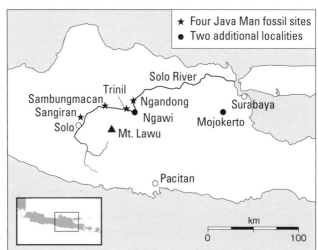

Fig. 2-7: Localities of interest, including four Java Man fossil sites.

Bengawan Solo drainage basin, though the river today is not very clean. The strata yielding the most Java Man fossils, however, are concentrated along its middle reaches.

Taking Solo with its international airport as our referent, to the northern part is the World Heritage site of Sangiran, the largest Java man fossil locality ("locality" being a technical term for a place where fossils are found). Sangiran is not actually located on the Solo proper but on the banks of a tributary only a few kilometers from the main channel.

Heading downstream east-northeast, you reach Sambungmacan,

Dr. Kaifu's excavation site. I came here in 2014 at Dr. Kaifu's invitation to join a Japanese–Indonesian team conducting a dig. Farther downstream is Trinil, and then Ngangdong, another important source of fossils and where lots of more recent Java Man fossils have been found.

Let's pause to review where we've been and recall the names of four Java Man fossil localities: (1) Trinil, the place of first discovery; (2) Sambungmacan, where Dr. Kaifu and his colleagues were doing their fieldwork when I joined them in 2014 to do research for this book; (3) Sangiran, the source of the largest number of Java Man remains and designated a World Heritage site in 1996; and (4) Ngangdong, where more recent fossils have been found.

Once you master these four "holy" sites, you'll have the basic map of Java Man in your head. If I could wish for more, then I'd have you add Ngawi, near Trinil, where the Java Man skull was found. Leaping farther afield, Mojokerto, near Surabaya, where the child's skull was found is also an important fossil locality for your mental map.

Bearing these four sites and two localities in mind makes you a true enthusiast. And all the better if you can also remember Pacitan, where no fossils have been found but many stone tools have been excavated. Among these Java Man fossil localities, one stands out by any parameter, whether by quality and number of unearthed fossils, estimated age, or length of time for yielded discoveries: Sangiran.

Deep in Onion Strata: Sangiran 17

I accompanied Dr. Kaifu on a visit to the Sangiran Early Man Site. At the entrance to the facility, refurbished in 1996 to commemorate its listing as a World Heritage site, we were first met by a giant Java Man head.

First encounter was the Stegodon at Trinil, and now a giant head. It struck me that there was something wondrously inviting if not soothing about the approaches to these Java Man museums. "That's probably intended to replicate Sangiran 17," observes Dr. Kaifu.

Sangiran 17. In the world of paleoanthropology, numbers are assigned to fossils in the order of discovery at a given locality. By this coding method, Sangiran 17 is the seventeenth Java Man fossil found at Sangiran. It's also the most famous and an extremely well-preserved specimen. "Sangiran 17 is the only *Homo erectus* skull fossil where the facial bones have also been preserved," Dr. Kaifu explained. "There are extremely

Fig. 2-8: Java Man head at the Sangiran Museum entrance.

few *Homo erectus* fossils found with the face intact." As the only fossil from which we can clearly understand the facial structure of *H. erectus*, Sangiran 17 has become the holotype for nearly every reconstruction of what Java Man looked like. The human who once bore this famous countenance might never have dreamed of such fame, but Sangiran 17 today has become the face of Java Man.

How is it that Sangiran has produced so many *Homo erectus* fossils and earned the World Heritage inscription of "Early Man Site"? The answer is to be found in the remarkable onion stratigraphy of Sangiran.

The understanding today is that after original sediment strata built up over millions of years in what would become the island of Java, pressure from underground magma activity forced a large area to rise into the dome of sediment of what's now Sangiran. Over time, the dome was worn flat by erosion with a remarkable result: the lowest and oldest layers of sediment were exposed at the surface of the former dome. Newer layers of sediment from the center outward were exposed in vast concentric circles. Thanks to this ancient uplift, it's possible to see examples of more than two million years of strata in nearly the same place. The strata in the center of the uplifted zone is the oldest, with more recent strata being exposed as you move out from the center.

That's the short story of the Sangiran onion. Seen from outside the uplift zone, the uplifted strata look like the top of an onion that has pushed partway up from the earth. Subjected to erosion, the elevated parts of this strata dome were worn flat, so what was left behind has the same concentric circular layers seen in an onion's cross section: the inner core would be the oldest sediment, and the outer layers consecutively newer sediment.

At Sangiran, this means we can sequentially track sediment from more than three million years ago—when the area that is now Java was the sea floor—up to about 250,000 years ago, when the sea became land.

Normally, if you were to try to study consecutive sediment layers over such a long period, you'd have to find either extremely high cliff faces or dig as deep a trench as possible. Alternatively, you might seek out different regions with exposed strata from different time periods and then painstakingly stitch your results together. Compared to that process, finding a place where you can travel across the ages in onion-like concentric circles just by walking across the landscape is a dream come true.

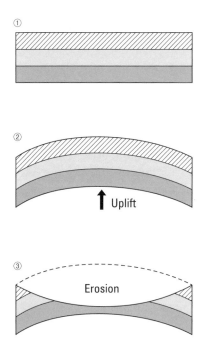

Fig. 2-9: Onion stratigraphy
Central area of uplifted strata (1) is eroded away (2). Moving out from the oldest stratum at the center, more recent layers are exposed in concentric circles like the cross-section of an onion.

The Man Who Ended the Missing Link Debate

The person who discovered that Sangiran was a treasure trove of *Homo erectus* fossils was German anthropologist Gustav Heinrich Ralph von Koenigswald (1902–1982). His search for fossils on Java began in the 1930s, and his research revealed the unique significance of Sangiran geology. In 1937, 46 years after Dubois' initial discovery, von Koenigswald succeeded in finding a skull fossil that closely resembled Dubois' Trinil holotype. In all he found three skulls, four jawbones, and much more, including more than 100 fossilized teeth. In the face of this overwhelming evidence, even the skeptics had no choice but to concede Dubois' old claim of a transitional fossil.

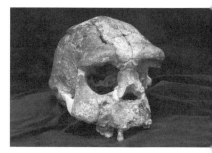

Fig. 2-10: Sangiran 17, with facial bones preserved.

What are we to make of these discoveries? Since the oldest Java Man fossils date back more than a million years, finding so many is entirely different than uncovering a trove of human bones from, say, a Japanese Jomon Period (16,000–1,000 BCE) site. Even given the remarkable geology of Sangiran as a fossil locality, you've got to wonder at von Koenigswald's incredible eye or nose for buried treasure.

As we stood in the museum, Dr. Kaifu without any forewarning pointed at a replica of a skull fossil on display: "You can see he reassembled this one after it had been broken." Looked at closely, this skull seemed to be run through with fine lines that couldn't possibly have been natural cranial sutures.

Fig. 2-11: A young von Koenigswald examines a fossil skull.

"The method von Koenigswald used to collect fossils was to rely on local people," Dr. Kaifu explained. "He'd tell them how much he would pay them for each individual fossil they brought him. So, what do you think happened? When one of the locals found a particularly good fossil skull, he smashed it and cheerfully brought the pieces

Fig. 2-12: Sangiran 2, assembled from 40 fragments.

to von Koenigswald to be paid for them. This is a replica of Sangiran 2, the skull that that was shattered into forty pieces." No doubt relying on the local eye was an efficient approach, and one that provided von Koenigswald with many fossils, but it also had its drawbacks.

"When villagers bring in a fossil they find, it's extremely hard to determine which sediment layer it had occupied," Dr. Kaifu explained. "The age of a fossil is usually assigned based on the age of the strata in which it's found. But when a fossil is brought in, you often can't tell which strata it comes from. That's why, in principle, anthropologists no longer use this method."

Another von Koenigswald anecdote relates to Japan and his specimens. During Japan's occupation of Java during World War II, von Koenigswald—who became a Dutch citizen to do research on Java—was held prisoner for 32 months in an Imperial Japanese Army internment camp. He carefully hid his fossils before internment, yet one Java Man skull— of comparatively recent vintage from Ngandong—passed into Japanese hands and was sent back to Japan as a gift to the emperor.

After the war, the Allied Occupation Forces discovered the skull where it had been put into storage, not even unwrapped, and after a long, long journey, it finally returned to von Koenigswald, where he was working in the United States. But this precious fossil's journey didn't end there. It later travelled to the Netherlands with von Koenigswald when he eventually returned home, before it finally made it back to Ngandong after a journey around the planet. There are many Japanese connections to the discovery and study of Java Man, and this story is the first entry in that record.

Into the Field, Feet on the Ground

You might feel overwhelmed when you first set foot in the field in Sangiran, that famous repository of *Homo erectus* fossils, but you soon find this World Heritage site is quite densely populated, its many residents working their fields. Wherever you look are classic vistas of rural landscape. When Dr. Kaifu and I visited, there were rice paddies everywhere, dry after the harvest, and row upon row of freshly planted fields. A Solo tributary runs through the district, and I found this halcyon vista of peaceful, terraced rice paddies along the river to be somewhat nostalgia-inducing.

Despite the tranquil appearance of rice cultivation, when you walk or drive through that landscape, you can see the different layers of strata and,

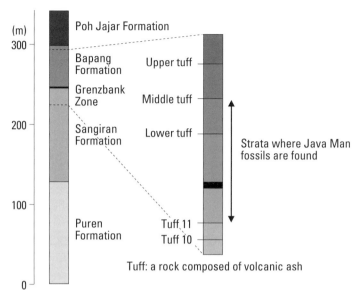

(m)
300

Poh Jajar Formation

Bapang Formation — Upper tuff

Grenzbank Zone — Middle tuff

200

Sangiran Formation — Lower tuff

Strata where Java Man fossils are found

100

Puren Formation — Tuff 11 / Tuff 10

Tuff: a rock composed of volcanic ash

0

Fig. 2-13: Stratigraphic chart of Sangiran dome.

in effect, travel through time. Sangiran may be farmland, but it's also a time machine.

There are outcrops with exposed strata wherever you look, and it's possible that fossils may be buried in any one of them. It is easy to see why locals discover so many Sangiran fossils. The atmosphere is one where it seems natural for an adult taking a short break from farm work, or simply some children out playing, to suddenly find a fossil.

"The Sangiran (Pucangan) Formation has sediment that is lacustrine [formed or growing in lakes or marshes], composed primarily of black clay," explains Dr. Kaifu. "Above it rests the Bapang (Kabuh) Formation, a layer of stream bed sediment. The layers where Java Man fossils have been found extend from the upper part of the Sangiran Formation to the middle of the Bapang Formation. This represents a period of some 400,000 years or longer. The boundary between the Sangiran and the Bapang Formations is slightly different from what you might expect—a hard layer mixed with gravel that's been especially named the Grenzbank Zone."

Lying below the lacustrine Sangiran Formation is the Puren (Kalibeng) Formation. This is quite hard sediment, and there are places near Dr. Kaifu's Sambungmacan excavation site where the same formation is exposed. If you're primarily interested in Sangiran's Java Man fossils, then focus on the strata from the upper part of the Sangiran Formation on up through the gravelly Grenzbank Zone and into the Bapang Formation. In that thick slice of some 40 meters of sediment is recorded information on the evolution of Java Man from approximately 1.2 million years ago to some 800,000 years ago.

The place we accessed was close to an outcrop of Bapang Formation sediment. There are places in Sangiran where sediment projects from outcrops, and it seems quite feasible that a section collapsed by wind or rain would bring fossils down with it. This makes the prospect of discovery both terrifying and exciting. Indeed, there are local farmers who walk around hunting for freshly exposed fossils. There have even been cases where fossils were found when farmers were simply working their fields.

It brought to mind a documentary produced by NHK, the Japanese national public broadcasting company, that included a reenactment of the moment when the villager credited with discovering Sangiran 17—that invaluable skull with intact facial bones—made his find. In the scene, the farmer was simply levelling a small outcropping with a hoe. Apparently, such things happen routinely around Sangiran.

After we'd been walking for some time, several young researchers from the Sangiran Museum who accompanied us on our field trip pointed excitedly at a spot along the river and started furiously taking notes. When I asked what they'd found, they told me it was the place where an important fossil find had been made.

"It was Sangiran 2," explained Dr. Kaifu. "The skull that was smashed into forty pieces." The discovery site was right on the river, close to a bamboo thicket where tall bamboo trees were being cut down. There may not have been any fields or paddies, but there was plenty of human activity going on. "We're close to the lowermost layers of the Bapang Formation here," Dr. Kaifu added. "There are places where the Grenzbank Zone is exposed as well."

Thanks to Dr. Kaifu's impromptu lesson, I finally noticed the difference in the strata. The color here was much darker than what we'd seen before, and it was hard to the touch. Important fossils have been discovered in the Grenzbank before, and it wouldn't be at all surprising if new discoveries were made someday here or at a similar site. Sangiran locals live surrounded by Java Man fossils.

It was amazing to realize we'd just walked from the upper and middle

Fig. 2-14: Looking up at an outcrop of Bapang Formation where Java Man fossils have been found.

Bapang Formation to the Grenzbank, the lowermost part of the formation. Even calculated conservatively, we had just travelled back through hundreds of thousands of years.

Surprising Contribution from the Land of Volcanoes

We walked across the cracked mud of dry rice paddies even closer to the center of the Sangiran dome than either the Bapang Formation or the Grenzbank Zone. Farmers here must be growing rice in paddies built with clay from the Sangiran Formation, clay originally formed in prehistoric lakes and marshes.

Then we began to ascend a low hill. Unlike our previous time travel back to the past, from the Bapang Formation into the Grenzbank, we were climbing up through the formation from the bottom, from the past forward. The Sangiran dome may be made up of concentric, onion-like circles of strata, but there are places where it's been carved away by flowing waters, and others where hills have been left standing. At the macro level, the different formations may be thought of as laid out in concentric circles, but at the micro-level everything is intertwined.

"This hill is the 'type site' for the Bapang Formation," Dr. Kaifu told me. "It's a very important place, the place where a Japanese-Indonesian team carried out the research that defined the Bapang Formation back in the 1970s."

So that was why Dr. Kaifu led me here. Japanese and Indonesian researchers have built a very constructive relationship since World War II, all mediated by the study of Java Man. The starting point for the relationship was joint research carried out in the 1970s and 1980s. At the time, a Japan-Indonesia research team organized by Dr. Naotsune Watanabe of the University of Tokyo was carrying out a detailed study of Sangiran stratigraphy. The team precisely analyzed the different strata providing dates that had previously been ambiguous.

"This is it!" Dr. Kaifu said suddenly, as we came up to an outcrop. He touched the surface with his fingertip. "This is tuff," he explained, "a layer of volcanic ash we use to determine the age of geologic formations. The field is tephrochronology, a way of dating that you could say is a Japan specialty. Finally identifying the age of sediment at Sangiran with Japanese technology was one of the joint team's major achievements, though people still debate the Sangiran ages today."

As one of the world's most volcanically active countries, Japan is a leader in developing the field of tephrochronology. The technique is widely used for setting the age of strata. There are strata layers composed of volcanic ash, and if you can identify which eruption of which volcano deposited that ash, that data can help determine the geological era of that strata.

Indonesia, like Japan, is a land of volcanoes, and there are many layers of sedimentary tuff that can be used for dating purposes, including strata layers related to Sangiran's *Homo erectus*. This is one reason a Japanese research team joined its Indonesian counterpart in the twentieth century and used tephrochronology to generate a Sangiran timeline.

No doubt the precise dating of Sangiran deposits will change somewhat as our techniques become more sophisticated. However, nothing can begin unless someone is willing to be the first to try, using whatever scientific tools are at hand. It was the 1970 Japan-Indonesia research team that took that first step. Research into Sangiran deposit dating initiated by Dr. Watanabe was further refined by Dr. Shuji Matsuura, a chronologist at Ochanomizu University. Meanwhile, the actual study of the Sangiran fossils was moved forward by Dr. Baba (former National Museum director, you'll recall, and Dr. Kaifu's former supervisor). Now Dr. Kaifu has taken up the torch to continue the work begun by his predecessors. Japan's involvement in the study of Java Man has been both long and deep.

In the Land of Java Man

I think we now have a pretty good understanding of how the giant onion strata works. Scattered here and there across a pastoral landscape are outcrops, and when you cut away at them, fossils fall out. It's a mysterious landscape where past and present seem to overlap. Fortunately, the sediment in Sangiran contains calcium carbonate minerals, optimal for the fossilization and preservation of prehistoric bones. This doesn't mean that everything was fossilized, and there are certainly other remains that simply rotted and became earth. We'd been looking up at hills from which fossils were found while walking above other fossils beneath our feet.

That was the image that stayed with me from Sangiran. I couldn't help but feel the thick, almost torrid presence around me of creatures living there about a million years before me, or more likely from 1.2 million years to 800,000 years ago. What kind of place was Sangiran back then? Java Man wasn't an agriculturalist, so the landscape couldn't have been agricultural, as it is today. "It's been said that Sangiran was a grassland environment," explained Dr. Kaifu. "But since we also find the teeth of animals like orangutans and tapirs, which are arboreal animals, it would seem there were scattered woodlands as well."

Grasslands. And, here and there, forest. Probably the ancient Bengawan Solo or its tributaries ran through it, and animals would gather on its banks. Standing out most on those prehistoric grasslands of vast vistas would have been Stegodon, walking slowly and majestically, its huge tusks swinging. Prehistoric rhinos also would have lived out on the plains. A view taking in megafauna like elephants and rhinos would have been exotic indeed, second in no way to the African veld of today. And then, the water's edge: a raucous place, full of foot traffic and danger.

We can imagine how the bucolic sight of hippos floating in the river as if relaxing in a bath, of a mother water buffalo and her calf coming down to the water's edge for a drink, could turn into a tense drama in a single jet spray of blood. An enormous crocodile, for example, lurking in the water, clamps its jaws down on a water buffalo calf, dragging it into the river. The crocodile might be a gharial with a long snout or a more common species (fossils of both have been found in Sangiran). Whichever it would have been, the water buffalo would soon have perished, and while the river might run red for a time, before long all would return to the same peaceful vista it had been before, as if nothing had happened.

This is my own imagining. But it is incontrovertible that all the creatures I just described were living in the same place, at the same time, as Java Man. What kind of life did Java Man lead in such a place? That's what I want to know.

Writing the Great Java Man Novel

Returning to the Sambungmacan excavation site after visiting Sangiran, I found myself imagining what kind of people the *Homo erectus* humans often referred to as Java Man were.

What we find at Sangiran, at Sambungmacan, and at other important localities comes down to bones. For that matter, we find only the fossilized bones of a few body parts, a skull here, a jaw there. If we match human fossils and animal fossils from the same strata, then we can see *H. erectus* humans were living in a world prowled by Stegodon, tigers, giant tortoises, crocodiles, and other megafauna. Because we also find fossils of creatures expected to inhabit biomes like forests, grasslands, and river banks, we can further surmise that *H. erectus* lived in a rich and varied environment. Since there are layers of volcanic tuff in the stratigraphy, it's certain they were inhabitants of a volcanic landscape of huge eruptions.

We also occasionally find simple stone tools. From this we can further infer these humans carried out tasks like cutting, scraping, and digging. The stone tools that we have confirmed so far come under the category of "amorphous flake" tools, but we've not found any of the shaped hand-axes discovered in Africa or elsewhere. Putting all these clues together, how well can we recreate the kind of life Java Man led?

Let's imagine that we've decided to write a novel with Java Man as the protagonist. First, as an initial character-building exercise, let's consider what our protagonist will look like. Thanks to Sangiran 17, the fossil skull that still retains its facial bones, we can envisage his face to some degree. We've found enough Java Man skull fossils by now to say with confidence that men and women had a massive bone extension above their eye sockets, almost like a visor, what paleoanthropologists call a "supraorbital ridge." However, as we've so far found relatively few skeletal bone fossils, we know little about Java Man's build or if there was significant sexual dimorphism. If we were certain of extreme dimorphism, for example, with males being much larger than females, we might write something like, "His massive body attracted some of the women." Based on our current knowledge, however, we know such a sentence would be absurd, out of the question.

It's even more hopeless to conjecture about

Fig. 2-15: An apparent stone tool excavated at Sambungmacan.

behavior and culture. How could we possibly describe the life Sangiran residents led—when they rose in the morning until they went to sleep at night—without solid evidence?

To begin with, what kind of place did they wake up in? A cave? Did they prepare simple bedding? What did they do after waking up? Would they go as far as their water hole to get a drink? Or did they have ways of drawing and storing water? For that matter, what kind of group composition did they have? Did adults practice organized hunting in large groups?

Fig. 2-16: The "old-school" Java Man diorama at the Sangiran Museum.

If this were a novel, we might write a thrilling scene where they hunt Stegodon. But we've no evidence of such hunting. Even if they could hunt prey the size of deer, when it came to the actual chase their techniques, too, would be fiction with no basis in fact.

A more promising narrative choice might be a hunt for a giant tortoise. It's not hard to imagine Java Man would consider it perfect prey. This is hypothetical, of course, as we are uncertain whether giant tortoises went extinct before or after Java Man's arrival. We simply do not have enough evidence to go on. There's a diorama of a Java Man family on display at the museum in Sangiran, but to recreate a scene imbued with such social context, we as authors would have to fill in the narrative gaps of what we know about Java Man. To begin with, we still don't even have a complete Java Man skeleton or know how age or sexual differences would have manifested.

The diorama scene depicting Java Man humans lighting a fire is a classic caveman stereotype that is easy to fall into. However, we do not have any evidence of fire use. At the very least, when it comes to Java Man's diet, it would be enough to find fossils of old bones and other detritus disposed of in one place after eating, like the shell mounds in Japan dating back to the Jomon Period. However, no such remains have been found in Sangiran, and there's no reason to think they will be. Shell mounds are evidence of fixed occupancy, so you can imagine the headlines if we did find evidence of them: "Java Man Lived in Permanent Settlements!" However, based on research on *Homo erectus* as well as Java Man, the prospects for such a finding seem slim.

I wonder if the day will come when extensive evidence related to Java Man culture and social behavior will be uncovered at Sangiran, the famed Early Man Site, or at the dig underway in Sambungmacan, or maybe even somewhere else. When I took these questions to Dr. Kaifu, his reply was that finding such evidence would be very difficult indeed, at least in the case of Java Man. And he further explained there are reasons this is so unlikely.

Why Are There No Signs of Life?

One prime reason for the unlikelihood of finding cultural and social evidence on Java Man is that we're looking at beds of sediment hundreds of thousands of years old, often more than a million years ago. Yet it also relates to why and how we found any Java Man fossils. "The vast majority of the strata in which we've found Java Man fossils, both in Sangiran and in Sambungmacan, are strata made up of sediment deposited by rivers," Dr. Kaifu pointed out. "Fossils are found in it because the original bones were carried along by river currents until finally being deposited in sediment on the river bottom." It's self-evident once you think about it. The places where Java Man fossils have been discovered to date are not where those humans were living.

Fig. 2-17: Canal bed where Sambungmacan 1 was discovered, just off the Solo River, 4 km downstream and east of the locality presently being worked.

Though we don't know their original location, we can derive some information about the fauna of their day from animal fossils found with Java Man. Since many outcrops I saw in Sangiran during my hike with Dr. Kaifu were a considerable distance from the current course of the Solo, it was hard to remember

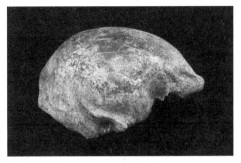

Fig. 2-18: Sambungmacan 1 skull.

they were sediment laid down by a river. A professional geologist might find my misunderstanding laughable, but until then, I had been under the vague impression that Java Man humans had resided where their fossils were found. In that respect, it's easier to remember you're looking at river sediment at the site of the Sambungmacan dig than it is at Sangiran. At that site, you can actually watch today's Solo River carving away at the sediment left behind by yesteryear's Solo.

Consider the place where Sambungmacan 1, the very first Java Man skull from Sambungmacan, was found. I'd heard Sambungmacan 1 had been discovered during construction work on a canal about four kilometers downstream from Dr. Kaifu's excavation site. I decided to go there. Upon arrival, I found the canal had been dug to provide a shortcut across one of the Solo's many meandering loops. It was dry season then, and the canal bottom was fully exposed, though I'd also heard river water poured through it during the rainy season. Apparently, it had been dug not as a way to speed up river traffic but as a flood prevention measure.

People were working on the nearby river when I reached the canal, and others were busily tending vegetable patches planted in the dry canal bed (their gardens no doubt to be submerged when the rains returned half a year on). They eyed me with curiosity.

Actually, this was the place where Sambungmacan 1 and Sambungmacan 2—a fossilized tibia (lower leg bone)—had been discovered. Work on dating these fossils is still underway, but both 1 and 2 appeared to be newer than those found in Sangiran and older than those from Ngandong. They'd been carried downriver from somewhere and deposited here, but their original "owners" had been living elsewhere. No wonder we haven't found traces of their owners' lives.

Another Mystery: Which Strata Did They Come From?

As if finding traces of Sambungmacan life is not enough of a problem, there's another complicating factor at work on Java. Rather than researchers discovering fossils themselves, it's much more common that fossils are brought in by the locals who find them. Time and again, it has proved impossible to determine the origin of the fossils. We've seen how this discovery process occurred at von Koenigswald's dig in Sangiran, but at least there he could ask the discoverers where the fossils were from.

In Sambungmacan, however, there are instances where even if you do ask the finders, they've no way of knowing—a serious problem. Sambungmacan 1, as previously explained, was found during construction work on the canal, and there is no reliable information on which layer of sediment it came from. Sambungmacan 2 was brought in by someone who simply found it lying on the ground and was then "discovered" back in Japan by Dr. Matsuura in a bundle of fossil material brought back to the National Museum as age analysis samples.

As for Sambungmacan 3 and 4, both were skulls that long, long ago had been washed along in an ancient river and finally buried deep in the sediment on the river bottom, there to eventually fossilize. Only recently had they tumbled from an outcrop of ancient sediment eroded by a modern river, plopped down into the water, and been washed along yet again until finally being discovered by locals who happened to be plumbing the Solo for sand. These patterns of discovery show how extremely difficult it is to determine the origin site as well as age of a fossil.

New York Java Man

Yet there was an even more unexpected discovery than the tumbling river skulls. Sambungmacan 3, the skull raised from the riverbed by sand excavators, was actually smuggled out of Indonesia. It wasn't until the specimen was offered for sale that researchers found out what happened.

"When overseas dealers gathered in Japan for the 1999 Tokyo Mineral Show, we were contacted by a New York antiques dealer," recalls Dr. Kaifu. "I guess they assumed the National Museum must have lots of money, because they brought along a skull replica to show us. They told us they had the original in New York and asked us to buy it."

A mineral show is where dealers gather to sell exotic minerals, some dealers offering fossils for sale. Welcome to the world of marketing fossils—originally living creatures—side by side with inanimate minerals. For the organizers of such shows, it's enough that both minerals and fossils are subterranean finds.

It isn't unusual for extremely rare fossils to change hands at these shows for astronomical prices. This, too, is standard, so long as everything is aboveboard and legal. However, there are instances of less savory transactions. Dr. Baba was heading up the Sambungmacan project when the museum was approached to buy the fossil. He immediately suspected a serious illegal act had taken place. As far as he could judge from the replica they'd been shown, there was little doubt the seller had a genuine Java Man skull. Moreover, in Indonesia today, it is illegal to take heretofore unknown Java Man fossils out of the country without permission. If the dealer's fossil was indeed the real thing, then it had to be illegal.

"Convinced that the skull was the real thing, Dr. Baba contacted the Indonesian team," Dr. Kaifu recounts. "He then secured the assistance of New York City's American Museum of Natural History to negotiate with the dealer. They ultimately succeeded in having the specimen returned to Indonesia. When it was subsequently examined to determine where in Indonesia it might have originated, it was determined to be from the area around Sambungmacan. It had been found on the riverbed about four kilometers from where Sambungmacan 1 and 2 had been discovered," Dr. Kaifu explained, adding, "That's not very far from where we are conducting our current excavation."

Fig. 2-19: Sambungmacan 3 skull, returned from New York.

That's the story of how the specimen later named Sambungmacan 3 was brought back successfully from the United States and went on to trigger a new excavation site along the Solo River. Later, another skull, Sambungmacan 4, was brought up from the riverbed a few hundred meters upstream from where Sambungmacan 3 was found. It seems fate does work in mysterious ways.

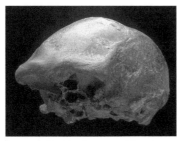

Fig. 2-20: Newly discovered Sambungmacan 4 skull studied by Dr. Kaifu and other research team members.

Sambungmacan 4 is an extremely well-preserved specimen, with even the fine, complex structure of the base of the skull preserved largely intact. The remarkable discovery created a stir when Dr. Baba, Dr. Aziz, Dr. Kaifu, and other team members published a paper on their find in the February 28, 2003, *Science* (Vol. 299, Issue 5611, pp. 1384-1388; DOI: 10.1126/science.1081676).

Extensive plumbing of the Solo River by locals in search of sand for concrete is so thorough that every year they scoop up nearly all the new sand washed down from the surrounding landscape and deposited on the riverbed during the previous rainy season. Combine that fact with the relative lack of damage to the skull, and it's clear that Sambungmacan 4 was carried down the Solo from some distant location over the course of many years. It was almost certainly washed up from sediment relatively close to where it was discovered.

Armed with this knowledge, Dr. Kaifu asked for help from Dr. Kazumi Yokoyama, a specialist in mineral analysis at the National Museum. He undertook the laborious analysis required to match the traces of soil adhering to Sambungmacan 4 with soils found in the vicinity of where it was discovered. Thanks to Dr. Yokoyama's work, Dr. Kaifu says they can now narrow down the area where the skull must have originated and derive a value for its age. There are plans to publish a paper on this discovery in the near future.

Given all the unknowns that remain and the little reliable scientific evidence on hand, we just can't reconstruct how Java Man lived. The day may come when we have a clearer understanding of this and more, but it's not likely to be anytime soon.

From a research perspective, then, which areas currently command the greatest attention? Which subjects are in greatest dispute? And what direction will research into Java Man take? After participating in the Java excavation for several days, digging up many fossils (albeit largely water buffalo bones), I was obsessed with such questions. To get the answers, it's time for us to leave the field and visit Dr. Kaifu's research facilities at the Division of Human Evolution in the National Museum's Department of Anthropology. What approaches are scientists using today to refine our study of fossil humans? How are they extracting data from the limited number of fossils we have at our disposal and using our knowledge of age-dating to find the answers? Let's return to the lab and see how these solutions are being pursued.

CHAPTER 3

Where It Happens:
Putting Science
to Work on Java Man

From Excavation to Contemplation

My visits to primary fossil sites such as Sangiran, Sambungmacan, and Trinil were invaluable experiences well worth having. The time spent there was remarkable, going onsite, seeing how the excavation work is done, and imagining what it must have been like to live in times past. It was thrilling to be at localities doing hands-on work in real time.

This field work is, of course, complemented by "minds-on" laboratory work far removed from the field and meant for bigger-picture contemplation. Efforts there are aimed at coming to grips with past realities—the true history of humankind. Much of this involves comparing and contrasting numerous fossil specimens. The idea is to carefully and objectively conduct vigorous debate, further pursue and develop ideas, and ultimately present one's findings to the world in scientific papers. In this sense, labs are the other frontlines for studying the history of humankind, and intellectual excitement is always lapping at the laboratory doors.

Until recently, research into Java Man had been confounded by a unique complication. Even if scientists tried to get an overall perspective on the specimens available, the specimen collections were scattered in many different locations, making it difficult for scientists to gain access to them. As a result, none of the world's researchers had been able to see all the significant Java Man fossils.

Although the situation has improved somewhat since the turn of the century, we're still a long way from an environment in which anyone can freely access all of these specimens. It would thus be extremely useful in terms of understanding overall trends if one could examine a large number of precision replicas these fossils, even if the actual fossils themselves are not available.

Fortunately, there is one place—but unfortunately only one place in the world—where this is possible: The Department of Anthropology at the National Museum in Tokyo. Through a series of historical accidents, the National Museum has come to function as a sort of Java Man research promotion agency. To tell the long tale of how this came about, we must go back to the original discovery of Java Man by Eugène Dubois.

Java Holotype at Home in the Netherlands

The holotype specimens for *Homo erectus* are the Java Man fossils first discovered in Trinil, in the early 1890s. They are of prime importance, historically as well as scientifically. Where are they now?

Their discoverer, Eugène Dubois, took them to the Netherlands, his homeland. They're now preserved in the Dubois Collection at the Naturalis Biodiversity Center Museum in Leiden, the country's largest natural history museum. In addition to crucial specimens of *Homo erectus* such as a skull, a left femur, and a molar, the collection includes a great many vertebrate fossils (mainly mammals) as well as Dubois' excavation notebooks.

The practice today is for specimens found in a country to belong to that country, but when Dubois made these discoveries, fossil finds were considered to be the property of their discoverer, even if he or she was a foreigner in the land of discovery. So it was unexceptional for the person finding them (Dubois) to assume ownership and take them home. This same practice applied to the other Trinil specimens as well, which is why they are also in the Naturalis in Leiden.

There are still many people who cite political instability and inadequate curation to argue that these priceless fossils should not be left with the countries where they are discovered, but the postcolonial consensus is increasingly affirming that discovery should not equal ownership and that they should stay as part of the site country's heritage. Either way, it is important every effort be made to avoid the tragedy that befell the Peking Man fossils which went missing during the Sino-Japanese War and have yet to be found.

First Sangiran Fossils Housed in Germany

What, then, became of the specimens from Sangiran, which yielded so many Java Man fossils? The initial specimens found by von Koenigswald, the site's discoverer, are not to be found in either Leiden or the local museum in Sangiran. So where are they?

Although a German citizen, von Koenigswald had taken Dutch citizenship while in Java to minimize the bureaucratic complications his excavation work entailed. As it was during the Japanese occupation of Indonesia, he was considered the citizen of a hostile power and sent to an internment camp. Had he retained German citizenship, he probably would have been treated as an ally and not interned, but he didn't and he was. Von Koenigswald succeeded in concealing most of his key specimens, hiding them himself or leaving them with people he trusted. While one comparatively modern Java Man skull from the Ngandong site was taken to Japan, as recounted in the previous chapter, it was eventually returned to von Koenigswald.

After the war, von Koenigswald departed Indonesia, found work at the American Museum of Natural History in New York, at Utrecht University in the Netherlands, and lastly at Senckenberg Natural History Museum in Frankfurt, Germany. The fossils he had found traveled with him wherever he went, so the specimens finally came to be stored at the Senckenberg Natural History Museum, the last place he worked. Even now this collection of Sangiran fossils, which doubtless held much personal significance for von Koenigswald, is curated there, including Sangiran 2, the skull that had been shattered into 40 pieces.

The only specimens found by von Koenigswald that made their way back to Indonesia were those from Mojokerto (Perning) and Ngandong, which he took home with the Sangiran specimens. These specimens were finally sent to Gadjah Mada University in Yogyakarta. While this may seem a triumphant return to their country of origin, there's more to the story than meets the eye. Since these specimens were originally discovered at excavations conducted by the Dutch Geological Survey, they should have been returned to its successor, the Centre for Geological Survey (Geological Museum) in Bandung. In the end, the Perning and Ngandong specimens were returned instead to a different institution, an incident that would later fuel antagonism among Indonesian research institutions.

Putting the Pieces Together

As Dr. Kaifu described the Indonesian human fossil research situation, "Indonesia doesn't have centralized control. When it comes to human fossils, Kenya, for example, has the National Museums of Kenya, where by law all fossils are to be preserved. The Philippines has enacted similar legislation, with authority in these matters vested in the National Museum of the Philippines. However, there is no comparable institution in Indonesia, so the different laboratories all maintain their own collections."

Many of the specimens relating to Java Man that remain in Indonesia are in the possession of Gadjah Mada University and the Centre for Geo-

Fig. 3-1: Sangiran 27 and 31, broken skull specimens in respective possession of the Bandung Institute of Technology and Gadjah Mada University. Fitting them together, Dr. Kaifu proved they're from one individual.

logical Survey. Other institutions have important specimens, including the Bandung Institute of Technology and the Sangiran Museum of Ancient Man. Relations among scientists in charge of these different facilities were strained throughout the twentieth century, making it difficult for researchers at any one institution to examine the specimens held by another institution. What had originally been scattered now came to be divided up as well.

However, Japanese researchers, including Dr. Baba, were able to forge good relationships with all the Indonesian researchers. Thanks to this diplomacy, Dr. Kaifu and colleagues have been able to work directly with nearly all original fossils and make precise replicas of them. They've also created replicas of the specimens held at the Senckenberg Natural History Museum, resulting in a situation in which precise replicas of Java Man fossils can be examined at the National Museum more comprehensively than anywhere else in the world.

Now a new generation has taken over leadership at the respective institutions in Indonesia, leading to a gradual resolution of the personal friction. This détente has been further promoted by international research efforts by Japan and others.

One incident is particularly telling. Dr. Kaifu identified two broken skull specimens held at two different institutions as actually belonging to the same individual. The specimens in question were at the Bandung Institute of Technology and Gadjah Mada University, despite having come from the same site at Sangiran. Both looked like thick rocks that had been crushed. Close examination revealed they were human bone fossils, but they were broken in a curious way, giving no clue whatsoever that they might possibly belong together. However, when Dr. Kaifu picked up both pieces, checked their alignments, and then tried fitting them together, it turned out those complex, cracked surfaces fit perfectly.

As is often said, there's no denying the evidence of one's own eyes. It was instantly clear for all to see that what scientists the world over had believed to be skull fragments from different individuals had in fact come from the same individual.

Dr. Kaifu and other Japanese scientists proposed to both institutions that they make and share precise replicas of their respective specimens. Moreover, he suggested they engage in joint research on the fractured skull, a proposal that was accepted by both parties.

Debuting in 2005 with Two Academic Papers

Since the turn of this century, the National Museum research team has published a series of comprehensive, detailed papers regarding Java Man. How did Dr. Kaifu find his way into this field and become one of its leading lights as group head of the institution's Division of Human Evolution? The story of the research that has brought him to such prominence is closely linked to recent developments in the study of Java Man.

"It all started in 1994, when my boss at the time, Dr. Baba, took me to Java," Dr. Kaifu recalls. "After that, having been initiated by such mentors as Dr. Baba, Dr. Matsuura, and Dr. Shuichiro Narasaki, I gradually began to pursue my own research and published my first results in 2005. That paper was sort of my official debut in the field of Java Man research. I'd actually gotten my findings together some time before that, but it took a while to publish."

In 2003, prior to debuting as a lead author, Dr. Kaifu participated in the analysis of the Sambungmacan 4 skull, with the findings published in *Science* magazine in a paper with Dr. Baba as lead author. The paper concluded that, based on comparisons with a relatively more modern Ngandong specimen (Ngandong 12) and an older specimen from Sangiran (Sangiran 17), the Sambungmacan 4 skull fossil displayed intermediate characteristics. At this point, Dr. Kaifu had already begun his signature detailed investigations of the specimens.

Then, in 2005, Dr. Kaifu made additional appearances in the form of two papers: "Hominid Mandibular Remains from Sangiran: 1952-1986 Collection" and "Taxonomic Affinities and Evolutionary History of the Early Pleistocene Hominids of Java: Dentognathic Evidence." Both were published in the same issue of the *American Journal of Physical Anthropology* (March 2005), a leading publication in the field. The first paper was a detailed report on specimen groups that had not been closely studied prior to that point, while the second presented a new interpretation of the evolution of early Java Man based on the first paper's findings and studies of other fossils.

The large quantity of specimens notwithstanding, no such comprehensive research had been carried out on Java Man fossils before this. Dr. Kaifu accordingly made a comprehensive study of found fossils, with particular focus on the especially numerous lower mandibles (jawbones) and teeth. He further compared these with *Homo erectus* specimens from China and Africa.

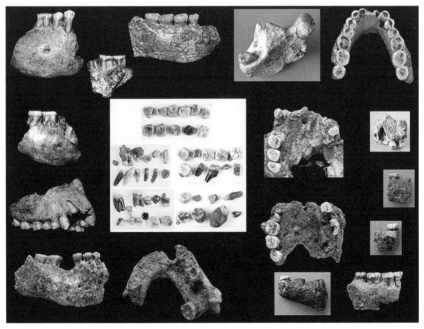

Fig. 3-2: A portion of the Java Man jawbone and tooth fossils analyzed by Dr. Kaifu.

When he showed me these papers, I finally understood why it took so long to publish. My impression of Dr. Kaifu is that he's a perfectionist who only wants to submit his work when he's satisfied that he's amassed absolutely all of the necessary evidence and has developed his arguments to the fullest extent possible. That inclination has been evident from his very first published work. That said, let's turn to what Dr. Kaifu was seeking to clarify.

Java Man Evolved

"The conventional wisdom about Java Man up to that time had been that the species had remained more or less static during the time it existed in Indonesia, hardly evolving at all," Dr. Kaifu says. "The perception was one of stasis in Asia compared to ever greater evolution in Africa. One reason was that, despite all of the fossils that had been found in Java, we didn't have a very clear idea of which periods they came from.

"It was right about then, though, that a group led by Dr. Matsuura, studying dating of different periods at Ochanomizu University, published its research findings indicating that this problem was being solved. I decided to use their research to study whether Java Man fossils from different time periods varied significantly. And if they were different, I wanted to know what aspects had changed and how."

The belief that Java Man had not evolved was based on "punctuated equilibrium," a theory that had gained currency in the last quarter of the twentieth century. The theory postulated that periods of dramatic, rapid evolution alternated with extended periods of stasis, or equilibrium, during which a species would remain relatively unchanged. The theory was primarily the work of Stephen Jay Gould, Harvard University professor and curator for invertebrate paleontology at the university's Museum of Comparative Zoology. Gould, a popular essayist on science, specifically cited Java Man as an example of a species that was in equilibrium, arguing that it had remained in stasis for a million years or more.

One reason Gould's theory was difficult to test was that, as mentioned, the ages of the Java Man fossils weren't well known. The first to finally shed light on this was a team of Japanese and Indonesian researchers working in the 1980s who used tephrochronology—a geochronology dating method using layers of volcanic ash as benchmarks and a Japanese specialty—to produce groundbreaking dating. A second study by a

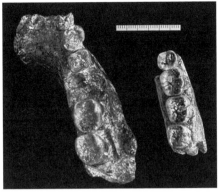

Fig. 3-3: Java Man lower jawbone fossils found at Sangiran. Sangiran 9 (approx. 1 million years ago), left. Bp8103 (approx. 800,000 years ago), right. The older fossil has larger teeth and a more robust jawbone.

research team at Ochanomizu University since the turn of the century has produced even more granular dating, opening new horizons in the field.

Meanwhile, Dr. Baba and Dr. Kaifu had been fortuitously given an opportunity to examine Java Man fossils in a more comprehensive manner than anyone had attempted up to that point. Moreover, they had the determination, the knowledge, and the skills needed for the task. The knowledge was the product of having brought together replicas of fossils of Java Man and other archaic hominins from all over the world for study at the National Museum. The skills Dr. Kaifu had gained through his work with Dr. Baba.

"One significant discovery was that Java Man had indeed changed," says Dr. Kaifu. "The fossils found at Sangiran show significant changes occurring over just several hundred thousand years. Tooth size in particular changed dramatically. Let me show you.

"This older jawbone," he continues, handing me the jawbone on the left in Fig. 3-3, "has more robust teeth. Compare it with this upper jawbone [on the right in the photo] from a higher stratum, in other words, a more recent layer. The difference in tooth size is clear at a glance."

I was startled by how casually Dr. Kaifu handed these items over. Of course, they were replicas and thus there was no real cause for concern, but they were still precision replicas, somehow exuding an atmosphere that they weren't to be carelessly handled. When I gingerly ran my finger across them and leaned in for a closer look, I understood for myself the point Dr. Kaifu was trying to make. No one examining these two specimens would think them the same size. They differed noticeably, both in the robustness of the jaw bones and in the size of the teeth. You could say it was a case of feeling-is-believing.

"Having changed as dramatically as it has, the newer jawbone already falls into the range of variation for *Homo sapiens*," Dr. Kaifu continued. "Or to phrase it differently, even among Sangiran fossils, teeth from the latter period some 800,000 years ago had already shrunk to within the size range of modern human teeth, albeit on the high end of that range."

This finding is particularly significant because shrinkage of the masticatory apparatus is considered an especially important indicator of the directionality of human evolution. It unequivocally states, loud and clear, that Java Man had not remained in stasis but had, in fact, evolved.

Five Hundred Modern Human Dental Casts

This was eloquently shown in Dr. Kaifu's paper. There are five objects to examine: first premolars, second premolars, first molars, second molars, and third molars. As upper and lower jawbones must be examined, this comes to a total of 10 types of teeth to be inspected.

There were no specimens with first molars intact in the upper jawbone from more recent geological layers, precluding any comparison with these. However, as Fig. 3-4 indicates, the other nine types of teeth display a clear tendency in which those from the more recent sediment layers are smaller than those from the older layers. The teeth examined here came from five individuals from the newer layers and 10 individuals from the older layers. Based on this, we can conclude that all five newer-layer indi-

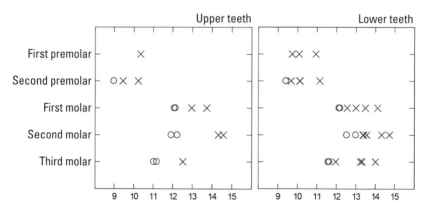

Fig. 3-4: Dr. Kaifu's comparison of Sangiran tooth size.
X-axis indicates tooth size, with larger values indicating larger teeth. "O" designates the more recent specimen group and "X" the older specimen group.

viduals had smaller teeth than the 10 older-layer individuals.

If there were no differences between the two groups, then the probability of such a result occurring by chance alone would be no more than 0.1 percent. Hence, it should be safe to say it's been demonstrated that reduction in tooth size over time did occur among the Java Man humans of Sangiran.

It's also apparent that the variation in tooth size among the Java Man specimens from newer layers of sediment in Sangiran falls within the natural range of variation in tooth size for modern humans. This, too, is a significant finding in terms of human evolution.

By the way, if you're curious about how the variation in tooth size for modern humans was checked, then you should know that Dr. Kaifu has collected plaster casts of the teeth of some 500 people from human groups all over the world and keeps them in his lab. "I made all of these myself," Dr. Kaifu told me. So saying, he showed me the cabinet in which the casts were stored, all carefully sorted. I found the sight a bit dazzling.

Imagine: Human beings have 32 teeth, including wisdom teeth. Even if you round that down to 30, then make 15 teeth for a cast of only one side of the jaw, it still works out to 7,500 teeth from 500 subjects. A tooth may be tiny, but collecting plaster casts of so many is extremely useful for researching modern humans and for data when discussing the story of human evolution. The young Dr. Kaifu went to museums the world over, making plaster casts of modern human teeth from collections in many

Fig. 3-5: Casts of early *Homo* jaws and teeth from around the world.

regions. And the only thing he said about this remarkable collection is, "I'm probably the only person in the world who has stuff like this."

Java Man Outstripped the African *Homo erectus*

"Another point of interest with regard to the teeth is that this reduction in size happened in Asia before it occurred in Africa," Dr. Kaifu continued. "The specimens I showed you date from 1 million to 800,000 years ago, and the teeth are smaller than in African specimens from the same time period. The dominant view until now was that Java Man remained in stasis, not evolving in the least, until ultimately going extinct 50,000 years ago. Now, however, we're finding that while Java Man did indeed die out, it's not the simple story previously thought of Africa leading the way while Asia lagged behind."

Overturn old preconceptions, and with them the whole landscape can change. Java Man, once held up as an example of equilibrium in the theory of punctuated equilibrium, was found—just by looking at its teeth and jawbones, the critical masticatory apparatuses— to have changed greatly over time. In fact, this change now appears to have happened earlier in Java Man than among the African *Homo erectus*.

Africa will always occupy a very special place in the history of human evolution. Make no mistake, the continent's importance is singular: it's where humankind branched off from the apes; the genus *Homo*, that first iteration of humankind to spread around the world, originated there; and *Homo sapiens* spread from there to populate the whole planet. But now it seems Africa was not necessarily the first in everything evolutionary.

The Great *Meganthropus* Debate

Large teeth fossils and very robust jawbone fossils have also been found from the older or lower layers of sediment in Sangiran. For a time, these finds led some to argue for the existence of a mysterious group dubbed *Meganthropus* ("the giant"). Since these fossils are exceptionally large and more robust than those from more recent strata, it makes you wonder what happened to make them that way. I thought Dr. Kaifu would have something new to share with me about these discoveries, given his comprehensive research into the Sangiran teeth.

"Hold the specimen in your hands," Dr. Kaifu encouraged me. "These

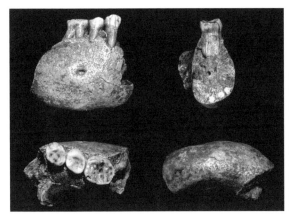

Fig. 3-6: Sangiran 6a (*Meganthropus* A), the fossil that started the debate. A lower jaw fragment with first and second premolars and a first molar. Teeth and jawbone are extremely robust; it's clear from the exposed jaw section, as seen from behind (upper right), the bone is extremely thick.

are a robust jawbone and teeth from a lower, older layer. Lots of hypotheses have emerged from examining this specimen. In particular, von Koenigswald, who carried out the first excavations at Sangiran, thought there must have existed a distinct genus, and he named it *Meganthropus*, as opposed to genus *Pithecanthropus*. The German researcher Franz Weidenreich, who studied Peking Man, believed *Meganthropus* was older than *Pithecanthropus*, and, what's more, he extrapolated from it that the ancestors of humankind had been giants. There truly have been a variety of hypotheses, such as the one holding that the jawbone belonged to a species equivalent to *Homo habilis* in Africa or that it was a relative of the robust australopithecines."

Due to the exceptional size of these specimens, the idea that they represented a form of gigantic human distinct from *Pithecanthropus* (or *Homo erectus*, as we now are calling them) was on everyone's lips at the time they were first discovered. In his 1946 work, *Apes, Giants, and Man*, Weidenreich inferred this was a type of human that predated *Pithecanthropus* and had been larger even than gorillas. Lay enthusiasts of cryptozoology and regular anthropology have added all kinds of embellishments. There is even one folklore notion that the mysterious creature must have been a giant that stood some 2.5 meters.

While the subject has been debated persistently in academic circles, the lack of definitive evidence has meant the mystery has remained for more than half a century, from the 1940s until today. How does Dr. Kaifu see the debate?

Dr. Kaifu's Stance on *Meganthropus*

"My research has revealed that Java Man changed over time," Dr. Kaifu says. "By Java Man, I mean *Homo erectus*, which in turn is the name given to the first skull found at Trinil, making that the holotype specimen. The question then becomes, do the large jawbone and the teeth found in layers older than that belong in this group or not?"

It's important to note that, while *Meganthropus* was found in strata from the lower layers at Sangiran and the Trinil type specimen is currently believed to be more recent, both *Meganthropus* and the Trinil-type specimen belong to the "early level" of *Homo erectus* when placed in the context of all Java Man specimens found to date, including the much more recent ones from Ngandong. The debate about their respective ages therefore concerns which of them is older among this early group, and not among Java Man finds overall.

"While examinations show the fossils are clearly more robust than other Java specimens, they also have many points of similarity," says Dr. Kaifu. "My thinking nowadays is that they are *Homo erectus.* They show such progressive characteristics as having somewhat smaller teeth than African australopiths and the like, and we also see a broadening of the dental arch. Hence, it seems to me that, at the very least, they cannot be australopiths, nor are they *Homo habilis* from around two million years ago."

In other words, there's no contradiction in treating *Meganthropus* simply as an early Javanese *Homo erectus*, and no reason to give it its own specific name. The thought that humankind had gigantic ancestors or that there once was a gigantic hominin species in addition to *Homo erectus* may fire the imagination, but we must proceed with caution.

Putting the Debate to Rest

There's another thorny aspect to the *Meganthropus* debate, as Dr. Kaifu pointed out. "The thing is," he said, "there are slender and robust jaw-bones being found together in the same strata where fossils claimed to be *Meganthropus* were found. "Here. This and this," he added, pointing to details in a photograph (Fig. 3-7). "If you compare these, you'll see that while both jaws have robust teeth, the jawbones themselves are different."

Speaking with Dr. Kaifu in his own lab gave me the opportunity to hold replicas of the fossils we were discussing, view them from all angles, and even feel the contours. This is great for facilitating understanding. Looking at and feeling the replicas, I could clearly tell there were two groups of older Sangiran lower jawbones: a robust jaw group, including Sangiran 6a and Sangiran 9, and a slender jaw group that included Sangiran 22 and Sangiran 1b. The jaws being different despite all of the teeth being quite large suggested this puzzle wouldn't be easy to solve.

"Normally, one might be inclined to treat these as separate, distinct species," Dr. Kaifu observed. "However, aside from the robustness of the jaws, they have features in common, which leads one to suspect they can't simply be designated as being distinct from one another. So we withhold judgment. If these aren't distinct species, then another possibility is that they signify a sex difference, that is, a significant difference occurring between males and females. Perhaps it was characteristic of ancient humankind for males to be robust and females gracile. It seems further investigation is called for, in this respect as well as others."

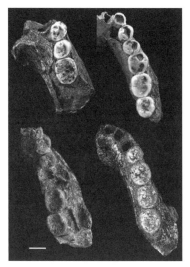

Fig. 3-7: Older lower jawbone fossils from Sangiran (scale at lower left: 1 cm). Clockwise, from upper left: Sangiran 6a, 22, 1b, and 9. The two left-hand specimens are robust, but the two specimens on the right are not.

The view that there may have been significant morphological sex differences among early *Homo* during the age of *Meganthropus* was as seductive to me as the notion of there having been two distinct human species. The idea of a species of giants and a species of ordinary people existing in the same era, as well as the idea that there had been a single species in which the males and females had been considerably different in size, stirred my imagination.

What kind of research would be needed to arrive at a satisfying conclusion? "There can be no ultimate resolution so long as we're limited to just jaws and teeth," said Dr. Kaifu. "The next step is to look at other parts of the body, and especially the skulls. I published a paper to that effect in 2010 in which I pointed out that, as with jawbones, there are robust and gracile specimens alike among skulls found in the lower layers at Sangiran. My personal prediction as of today is that there's a high probability this represents a sex difference. We now have conditions in place where we can conduct research on additional specimens, and I plan to do this. There are still some fossils that have not been studied properly. While thinking on this, I've been bringing these to Japan and scanning them to produce precision replicas."

Creating 3D Data from Specimen Scans

Now that the subject of acquiring 3D data from CT scans and creating precise replicas based on that data has come up, let's take a short detour and see how this is done.

In the closing days of 2015, I received an email from Dr. Kaifu. "We're making CT scans," the message read. "Would you like to come and watch?" This time we would be meeting not at the Tsukuba research facility but at the National Museum. I immediately headed for Ueno, in Tokyo.

Just past the dinosaur exhibit in the Global Gallery, some 10 meters from the *Tyrannosaurus* skeleton, there's an area with glass partitions allowing gallery visitors to watch what's happening inside. This is where CT scanning is carried out.

Entering the CT scanning room, the first things I noticed were a huge old-fashioned leather bag and a collection of specimens arrayed on a desktop (Fig 3-8). "These specimens are from Gadjah Mada University in Indonesia," Dr. Kaifu explained. "They travel as carry-on luggage in this leather bag and are taken back home the same way once we've taken the micro-CT scans."

True, it wouldn't be wise to entrust precious specimens like these to airline check-in or one of the delivery services. The leather bag was something of an antique, carefully padded with cushioning. The specimens casually arranged on the desk were all originals, including two complete skulls.

Dr. Kaifu described each specimen for me. Following are his descriptions, in the order in which the specimens appear in Fig. 3-8, right to left and front to back. In the front right are two tibias (shin bones) discovered at Ngandong (the locality yielding relatively "modern" Java Man fossils). At front center are the pieces of the damaged skull which, as I mentioned previously, Dr. Kaifu was the first to realize were actually from a single individual, rather like the pieces of a 3D jigsaw puzzle. The fossil in the middle

Fig. 3-8: CT scanning room, National Museum of Nature and Science, Tokyo. Desktop is packed with genuine fossil specimens.

Fig. 3-9: Skull from Bukuran, Sangiran region.

Fig. 3-10: Child's skull from Mojokerto.

of the tray belongs to Gadjah Mada University, while the piece on the left belongs to the Bandung Institute of Technology. However, for various reasons, it is currently held, against the Institute of Technology's wishes, at Gadjah Mada University. Thanks to Dr. Kaifu's mediation, however, relations between these two institutions have thawed considerably and they have agreed to participate in joint research with the National Museum.

At the rear of the array of fossils, from right to left, a skull from Bukuran (a Sangiran district), a child's skull from Mojokerto, and an unnumbered jawbone specimen known only as Mister X. All in all, it was quite a selection, certain to excite the true aficionado. It turned out that many of the best-known Java Man specimens had been scanned already, including Sangiran 17 with its remaining facial bones and the Sambungmacan skulls Dr. Kaifu helped discover.

New Research Methods with Better Digitalization

Dr. Reiko Kono, a paleoanthropologist at Keio University, had completed the preparations for the scan by the time I arrived. She is steeped in applied research into human fossils using micro-CT scanning and has scanned a great many in her career, including the majority of Java Man specimens Dr. Kaifu brought to Japan for research.

The micro-CT scanner was encased in housing about the size of a soundproof booth for home use. Radiation warning stickers on the outside indicated it was a radiation-controlled area, and there was an illuminated warning sign that lit up whenever scans were underway.

Fossil specimens are set up inside the scanning room, but in this case, the procedure is unlike what you or I might typically imagine when we hear the term "CT scan." In the case of CT scanners used in medical settings, both the X-ray source and the X-ray detector are mounted on a ring-shaped gantry. The patient lies on the examination table and is passed through the ring. A continuous scan of the patient's body is taken as the X-ray source and X-ray detector paired in the gantry rotate constantly. In short, it's the apparatus, not the subject, that's rotated.

In the case of micro-CT scanners, however, the reverse is true. They were originally developed for product quality inspection, with X-ray source and detector anchored in place while the object being inspected is rotated on a turntable. With the turntable positioned between the cylindrical X-ray source and the white sensor portion, it looks very much like a

Fig. 3-11: The National Museum's microfocus CT scanner.

typical X-ray machine. And that's exactly what it would be if it didn't rotate the subject while taking images from all angles. The point is to make solid interior structures visible by taking X-ray images from multiple angles.

I watched the Mojokerto child skull being scanned. Wrapped in black padding, it was gently anchored in place in a transparent cylinder to prevent shifting. The settings, like optimum distance from source and sensor, depend on the size of the object and other factors. Once those adjustments are made, the scan commences. And then everyone waits. It took a full two hours for the scanned data, controlled to a precision of 250 microns, to be transmitted to the computer and digitally reconstructed into a 3D image of the child's skull. I was told the work takes a lot of time because the subject is rotated gradually and is scanned bit by bit.

Fig. 3-12: The National Museum CT scanning room, visible to museum visitors through a glass partition.

The image that finally appeared on the display was so brilliant and clear that I was transfixed. As it was 3D data, the image could be rotated with the mouse, enabling one to view it from all directions in various sizes. Cracks where the fossilized skull had been fractured could be clearly distinguished from the original cranial sutures. Complex structures at the base of the cranial vault housing the brain could also be distinguished in detail. No doubt it was also possible to precisely measure brain size.

Fig. 3-13: Cylinder on the right contains the Mojokerto child skull, wrapped in black padding.

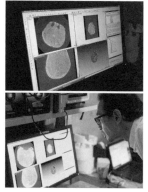

"It's still important to have an original or a replica at hand to view and to contemplate," stressed Dr. Kaifu. Having such digital data will open the door to new research techniques. Even replicas can be mass-produced from the scanned data at the required levels of precision using 3D printers.

Fig. 3-14: Top: 3D image of the scanned Mojokerto child skull. Bottom: Dr. Kaifu examines the image.

Determining Brain Size with 3D Data

Dr. Kaifu and his colleagues are currently using the 3D data obtained with the micro-CT scanner to develop methods for compensating for missing portions of partial skulls and estimating brain size. This research is being conducted jointly with Dr. Daisuke Kubo of Hokkaido University and researchers at the National Institute of Advanced Industrial Science and Technology. While the findings have yet to be published, word is that they expect to obtain quite positive results.

"I started this because I wanted to accurately know the brain size of Java Man," Dr. Kaifu said. "Until now, we've relied on the work of U.S. researchers done in the 1980s for this information. They reconstructed damaged skulls in a craftsman-like manner and derived brain size based on that. When our group took our own measurements, however, we wound up with many conflicting results. That wasn't satisfying, so we—especially Dr. Kubo—developed a method that would get us answers with the precision of just a few percentage points plus-or-minus. Nowadays, skulls I'd thought must have smaller cranial capacities than had been reported previously are indeed giving us smaller values. We're seeing more clearly that skulls from lower layers are yielding smaller cranial capacities, while those from the upper layers are proving to have larger cranial capacities." This detailed research could well lead to a reassessment of Java Man brain size.

Increasing Brain Size as Seen in Skulls

Now that we've looked into research using micro-CT scanners, let me return to the original subject. Dr. Kaifu's findings on Java Man skulls as of 2008 were published in the *Journal of Human Evolution*, another leading publication in the field, under the title "Cranial Morphology of Javanese Homo erectus: New Evidence for Continuous Evolution, Specialization, and Terminal Extinction." Of all the papers published to date, this paper most clearly indicates the position of Java Man in evolutionary history.

"We analyzed twenty-one Java Man skulls," explained Dr. Kaifu. "They came from Sangiran, Trinil, Sambungmacan, and Ngandong. In terms of time periods, the oldest ones came from the Sangiran formation in the lower layers at Sangiran, as well as from Trinil. They were followed by specimens from more recent layers at Sangiran, that is to say, the Bapang formation, and after that specimens from Sambungmacan and Ngandong."

A Japanese-Indonesian research team was the first to carry out a proper dating of the Sangiran stratigraphy, and the group at Ochanomizu University has been continuing that research. Work is currently underway to establish a chronology for geological layers pertaining to Java Man, including those at Trinil and Sambungmacan.

When it comes to the approximate ages of Java Man fossils, those found in the Sangiran formation at Sangiran are debated as dating from either 1.6 million or 1.2 million years ago, while fossils from the upper layers of the Bapang formation are thought to range from about one million to 800,000 years ago. While the age of the Sambungmacan fossils is uncertain, there are suggestions they date back to some 300,000 years ago. The age of the Ngandong fossils is also unclear, but there's a strong probability they date from about 100,000 to 50,000 years ago.

If we divide all specimens into three groups, they can be classified as in Fig. 3-15 into early-period Java Man (Sangiran, Trinil), middle-period Java Man (Sambungmacan), and late-period Java Man (Ngandong). The time periods would be approximately 1.2 million–800,000 years ago,

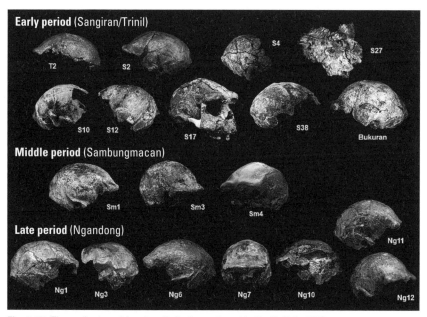

Fig. 3-15: The main Java Man fossil skulls analyzed in Dr. Kaifu's 2008 paper.

300,000 years ago, and 100,000–50,000 years ago. There is presently a 500,000-year gap between the early and middle periods because we haven't found any Java Man fossils from this time.

Of the fossil skulls used in the research, one was the Trinil skull that became the Java Man holotype specimen (T2), eight were from Sangiran (Series S and Bukuran), and three from Sambungmacan, the location of Dr. Kaifu's excavation (SeriesSm). "Series Sm" refers to

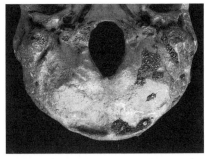

Fig. 3-16: Sand adhering to the bottom of the Sambungmacan 4 skull. Dr. Kaifu and his colleagues analyzed this sand when seeking the stratigraphic origin of this skull, as noted in Chapter 2.

specimens that Dr. Kaifu and his National Museum predecessor, Dr. Baba, were involved in discovering. These include Sambungmacan 3, the skull recovered from a New York antiques dealer, and Sambungmacan 4, discovered close to where Sambungmacan 3 is said to have been found originally. There are also nine skulls in all from Ngandong (Series Ng), considered to be among the most recent specimens of Java Man.

Java Man and Modern Man Followed the Same Path

The key to this research was the comprehensive examination of the morphology of many different specimens. Looking closely at Fig. 3-17, you'll see that 43 spots were studied. Quantifying the results derived for all these individual specimens was nerve-wracking. Not all specimens were on hand, so research involved traveling all over the world.

The paper's authors took each specimen—all originals, not replicas—in their own hands and measured them. They did not rely on data from other papers and they used the same method every time. It was essentially all done by hand. In instances where the points to be measured were unclear—due to the state of the fossils themselves or for other reasons—they made an extraordinary effort to get the measurements, sometimes drawing also on micro-CT scans to complete their work. The title of the paper shows what they found: "New Evidence for Continuous Evolution, Specialization, and Terminal Extinction."

"We drew the conclusion about continuous evolution by recognizing continuous morphological changes from the early to the late periods," Dr. Kaifu said. "For an older one, look at this replica from Trinil: It has a small cranial capacity, low head height, and very narrow forehead. Conversely, even at Sangiran, the more modern Sangiran 17 shows the forehead gradually getting broader. The tendency continues with the later Sambungmacan and Ngandong specimens. And the more modern Ngandong skull has an even broader forehead and a head that is more definitely rounded. Brain size is also clearly increasing."

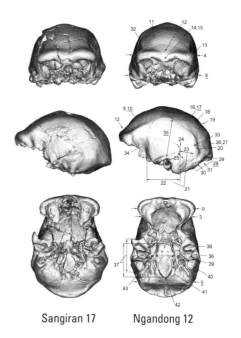

Sangiran 17   Ngandong 12

Fig. 3-17: Skull characteristics.

It was already known that Java Man's brain size had increased slightly over time. Painstaking investigations by Dr. Kaifu and his colleagues showed that there were various changes in all parts of the skull. The pattern that emerges appears to be that the skull is not just getting larger. The narrow forehead got broader, the skull became more rounded, the base of the cranial vault lengthened laterally, and the exterior portions of the supraorbital ridges (visor-like protrusions over the eyes) grew thicker.

I reiterate that Java Man was believed to have been in stasis for well

Fig. 3-18: Skull comparison
Early-period Sangiran skull is low with a narrow forehead, while later-period Ngandong skull is higher and has a broader forehead. Middle-period Sambungmacan skull is low but has a wider forehead.

Sangiran 17   Sambungmacan 4   Ngandong 12

over a million years. Dr. Kaifu, however, first verified the shrinkage of the masticatory apparatus and then showed that the shape of the skull had also gone through considerable changes. The enlargement of the brain and widening of the forehead are evolutionary directions Java Man had in common with *H. sapiens*. In other words, it's clear that Java Man also traveled the path taken by genus *Homo*, at least partially. While there are other highlights, it's notable that at least brain size and masticatory apparatus, the greatest features of interest in human evolution, clearly evolved.

Support for the Out-of-Africa Theory

Research showing that Java Man, previously believed to have been in stasis, did in fact evolve also contributes essential information to scenarios of human evolution and dispersal.

Homo habilis, the earliest *Homo*, evolved from African *Australopithecus* around 2.5 million or more years ago. Some time later, groups of early *Homo* left Africa. The oldest such evidence is Dmanisi Man, circa 1.8 million years ago, fossils of which were found at Dmanisi, an archeological site in Georgia, between the Black Sea and the Caspian Sea. Primitive and small of stature, its precise relation to *Homo erectus* is not entirely clear. However, it's an extremely important find in terms of tracing the route early *Homo* took out of Africa. Speaking very roughly, *Homo erectus* established themselves in Java by about 1.2 million years ago (1.6 million, by other hypotheses). Though isolated from other populations, Java Man thereafter exhibited changes characteristic of genus *Homo* like enlarged brain size and reduced masticatory apparatus.

Here, then, is my naive question: Now that we know Java Man evolved normally, as a member of genus *Homo*, if it had grown even closer still to us humans today, wouldn't it have evolved to a level considered late archaic *Homo* or even modern humans?

The relatively recent Java Man fossils excavated at Ngandong were first dubbed Solo Man, classified by some researchers as "early *Homo sapiens.*" Von Koenigswald referred to them as "tropical Neanderthals" from his belief that Solo Man represented the same level of development as Neanderthals.

There was and may still be debate about whether Java Man evolved into today's indigenous Australians and whether modern East Asians evolved from Peking Man. This is the concept known as the Multiregional

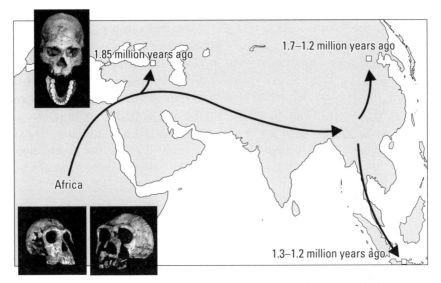

Fig. 3-19: When *Homo erectus* reached different parts of Asia after leaving Africa.

Hypothesis discussed in Chapter One. Does the research by Dr. Kaifu and his colleagues support this theory?

"No, quite the reverse," says Dr. Kaifu. "My research reaches a conclusion supporting the prevailing Out-of-Africa Theory. While I said Java Man also evolved, there are many characteristics unique to Java Man, and they steadily become more prominent. If Java Man were the ancestor of the indigenous Australians, these characteristics should have been inherited by them as well, but there's no sign of them in indigenous Australian peoples." Here, then, is the meaning of "Specialization and Terminal Extinction" in the paper's title.

Tracking Forms of Specialization

"Brace yourself, because this is going to get a bit detailed," warned Dr. Kaifu. "The unique specialization in Java Man is found in aspects such as the area of the temporomandibular joint, which has a most unusual morphology, although that example might be a bit too minute, I admit."

Dr. Kaifu pointed to a hollow at the bottom of the cranial vault (base of the skull) which is the attachment point for the lower jaw (Fig. 3-20). It is a very minute feature, hard to spot unless you look closely. Yet even so, it is a focus of interest for researchers who examine morphologies.

"In the temporomandibular joint in *Homo sapiens*, the aft portion of this hollow, the glenoid cavity, curves downward," Dr. Kaifu explained. "In fact, that is characteristic of all ancient humankind and is even present in Java Man fossils from Sangiran. But it has disappeared in more recent fossils from Ngandong. It's a minute point, but when you look at things like this, they all lead to Java Man having evolved in a different direction from *H. sapiens*. That makes it hard to think of them having been ancestors for *H. sapiens*."

There are other characteristics that scientists take as indicators of Java Man's specialization, but discussing them here would require an unusual degree of expertise. Among the 43 detailed traits on which Dr. Kaifu has focused his attention, many are signifiers about such fine details as frontal, parietal, temporal, and occipital bones; attachment points for temporal muscles; and the cranial base, in addition to such general indicators as those pertaining to measurements and overall size.

Let me give you some very popularized examples of some new findings.

The upper edge of Java Man's temporal bone is straight, like that of other *Homo erectus*, and this holds for the more recent Ngandong specimens as well. In more advanced forms of *Homo* including *Homo sapiens* (modern humans), the same edge is arched. Conversely, there are other changes not seen in other human species, including a steady thickening of the supraorbital ridge exterior and the central part of the cranial vault base becoming extremely extended laterally.

With a careful explanation and a side-by-side comparison of the speci-

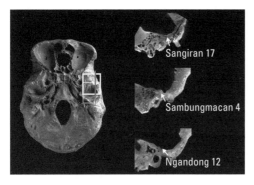

Fig. 3-20: Changes in the glenoid cavity in early-, middle-, and late-period Java Man skulls. Cross-sections on the right are CT scan enlargements of the boxed area in the image on the left. Changes in bone structure are indicated by arrows.

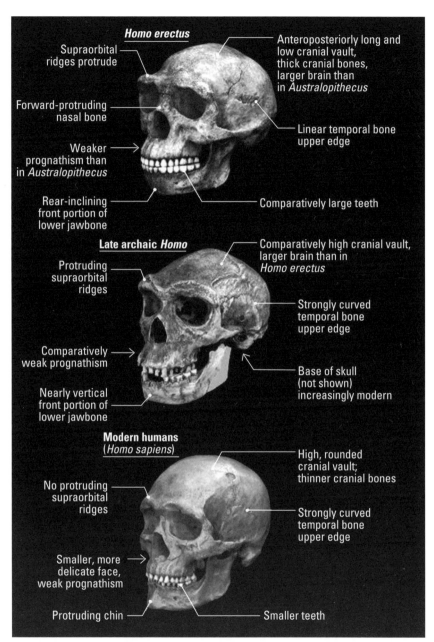

Homo erectus

Supraorbital ridges protrude

Forward-protruding nasal bone

Weaker ⟶ prognathism than in *Australopithecus*

Rear-inclining front portion of lower jawbone

Anteroposteriorly long and low cranial vault, thick cranial bones, larger brain than in *Australopithecus*

Linear temporal bone upper edge

Comparatively large teeth

Late archaic *Homo*

Protruding supraorbital ridges

Comparatively ⟶ weak prognathism

Nearly vertical front portion of lower jawbone

Comparatively high cranial vault, larger brain than in *Homo erectus*

Strongly curved temporal bone upper edge

Base of skull (not shown) increasingly modern

Modern humans (*Homo sapiens*)

No protruding supraorbital ridges

Smaller, more ⟶ delicate face, weak prognathism

Protruding chin

High, rounded cranial vault; thinner cranial bones

Strongly curved temporal bone upper edge

Smaller teeth

Fig. 3-21: Primary characteristics of skulls of *Homo erectus*, late archaic *Homo*, and modern humans, from a permanent exhibit at the National Museum.

men replicas, it all became clear. I am continually impressed by what sharp eyes the experts have. But discussing each of these individual aspects is only part of the process. The true pleasure of science comes in contemplating all these characteristics, refining the data to a state where a quantified argument can be made, and then arriving at a comprehensive conclusion.

As a result of investigating the new findings described above, science has concluded that Java Man was indeed undergoing specialization in a direction different from that taken by *Homo sapiens* (modern humans).

If you only look at Java Man's evolution in terms of larger brain size and smaller masticatory apparatus, it might seem to suggest a high degree of conformity with the Multiregional Hypothesis. Viewed in detail, however, many other characteristics emerge alongside these that are not found in us modern humans, making it unreasonable to consider them to be our direct ancestors. If anything, the Out-of-Africa Theory has been reinforced.

The theory that the common ancestor of *H. sapiens* originated in Africa has also been well-established in the late twentieth and early twenty-first centuries by DNA analyses in the new field of genetic anthropology, as well as by new fossil discoveries. Evidence from various fields converges on this theory, suggesting that it's unlikely to be overturned in the future.

However, while providing one solid piece of evidence in this debate, Dr. Kaifu's research results are a significant finding in their own right. To put it bluntly, the Multiregional Hypothesis holding that the East Asian *Homo erectus* (i.e., Peking Man) evolved into modern East Asian peoples, and that Java Man evolved into indigenous Australians, frequently had cited Java Man as an important piece of supporting evidence. There were researchers who made a morphological argument that Java Man and indigenous Australians look alike, and therefore the question of whether Java Man could have been a direct ancestor of *Homo sapiens* was important. Dr. Kaifu's research has definitively put paid to such a connection, leaving the Multiregional Hypothesis with even less ground to stand on. The question is still important, but the answer is "No."

Further Questions for Java Man Research

I hope I've succeeded in communicating where we stand in Java Man research here in the early twenty-first century, as well as new findings in that field. There are other known findings extending the inquiries we've made thus far that haven't been published. Dr. Kaifu listed some of the questions about Java Man that he thinks still need to be answered:

- ➢ When did Java Man first appear, and how diverse were they?
- ➢ Will the *Meganthropus* debate finally be settled?
- ➢ What were Java Man's physical characteristics, behavior, culture, and habitats?
- ➢ Are Java Man and Peking Man related in phyletic evolution terms?
- ➢ How does Java Man relate to *H. sapiens*?
- ➢ When and how did Java Man go extinct?
- ➢ Could Java Man have interbred with *Homo sapiens*?

While we have partial answers to some of these questions, there's a need even in those instances for clearer, sharper, higher-resolution comprehension than we have today.

I am personally keenly interested in the behavior, culture, and habitat questions. Though it hasn't been possible to pursue such inquiries with the research performed to-date, which has primarily been morphological studies of the fossil record, Dr. Kaifu is also engaged in archeological collaborations with experts in stoneware that could yield some positive results within the next several years.

Another profound question concerns how Java Man relates to Peking Man. Was there really no contact at all between them for over a million years, despite their both being in Asia?

Then there's the question of Java Man interbreeding with *Homo sapiens*. One subject of significant interest has been the recent finding that a small percentage of Neanderthal DNA is present in the modern human genome. Other research has shown that the Denisovans, thought to be an archaic *Homo* lineage distinct from Neanderthals, also interbred with us *Homo sapiens*. Indeed, some research shows segments of Denisovan DNA present in modern Melanesians.

There seems to be a strong possibility that *H. sapiens* and Java Man coexisted as well in Java during Java Man's final period. The question of whether interbreeding occurred as it did with the Denisovans makes for a thrilling research subject. This research will require not only morphological studies but also genetic anthropology. Perhaps the day will come when we'll be able to extract DNA fragments from Java Man fossils.

All of this is for the future. I expect Dr. Kaifu will likely establish a united front with scientists in other fields as well as in his specialization to attack these problems from many directions. And another huge subject intrudes into his research: Further east, in the Indonesian archipelago, a stupendous discovery has been made that upends the received wisdom of anthropology. The discovery is Flores Man. *Homo floresiensis*. The hobbit. Found in 2003 by an Australian-Indonesian team, this remarkable human species was first revealed in *Nature* magazine (2004), standing the world on its ear. And now Dr. Kaifu, whose research findings on Java Man have made their mark, finds himself participating in the study of *Homo floresiensis* as well.

CHAPTER 4

Grand Entrance from an Island Cave

H. floresiensis: Small Human of Immense Stature

In 2003, a discovery was made in a cave—Liang Bua Cave—on the Indonesian island of Flores that had the potential to upend our fundamental understanding of human evolution.

The skeleton of what appeared to be a primitive form of *Homo* was excavated nearly intact from a depth of six meters below the floor of a cave known for yielding stone tools and animal fossils. The specimen is now known as LB1 (Liang Bua 1). In addition to being almost complete from head to toe, the skeleton included such fragile and delicate features as facial and scapular bones. You'll recall the only Java Man fossil ever discovered with a significant portion of intact facial bones is Sangiran 17. In fact, it's rare to find an early human fossil with intact facial bones in Asia. Even in the case of Peking Man, where numerous skulls and jaws have been found, only small fragments of facial bone have been discovered.

The Australian-Indonesian team that made the discovery published a paper in 2004 (*Nature* 431, 1055–1061) proposing that LB1 be considered the holotype specimen for a new species of genus *Homo*, which they called *Homo floresiensis*. This announcement caused a sensation in aca-

Fig. 4-1: Reconstruction of *H. floresiensis*. Coexisting animals are rendered in life-size proportions.

demia and beyond, especially with the adoption of "hobbit" as its moniker, which seized the public imagination.

The key points of the 2004 paper are:

➢ The specimens date back between 38,000 and 18,000 years ago.
➢ They are from a new species of genus *Homo*.
➢ They were unusually small, a little over one meter tall.
➢ They lived on Flores Island, which never had a land bridge to the continent.

Any one of these points would have been shocking by itself. What drew me in was the paper's assertion of the date, which would put the find almost within the scope of history rather than science. In Japan, those dates correspond to late Paleolithic, just before the dawn of the prehistory of the Jomon period (16,000–1,000 BCE) when *H. sapiens* was flourishing in Asia.

These dates are far more recent than when Neanderthals went extinct approximately 40,000 years ago. This suggested to me that Flores Man might be the strongest candidate yet for a different human species that we modern *Homo sapiens* could have met but, in the end, did not. We can say with some confidence that modern humans would have crossed over to Flores by this comparatively recent date, which means that *H. floresiensis* and *H. sapiens* would have coexisted on the island.

I should hasten to add that this figure of 18,000 years, specified in the 2004 paper, was subsequently revised in a 2016 paper. As of this writing, the time when the skeleton was snug in its geologic layer has been estimated to be no more recent than 60,000 years ago. Even considering the layers in the cave where stone tools have been discovered, it seems *H. floresiensis* could not have been in Liang Bua Cave more recently than 50,000 years ago.

None of which detracts from the significance of the discovery itself.

In the words of Dr. Kaifu, well-versed in human evolution in Asia thanks to his Java Man research and to participation in the study of *H. floresiensis*, the thing to remember is that "a totally unexpected human species was found in a completely unexpected place."

I think it best to let Dr. Kaifu further explain the discovery in his own words: "It happened in a place where no one imagined there had ever been ancient humans," he told me. "Flores is along the route that *H. sapiens* took from Africa to Australia, and yet there was a group of these primitive humans still living there when *H. sapiens* arrived. I had personally believed it was only after the emergence of *H. sapiens* that the Wallace Line was finally crossed. It wouldn't have been possible to cross open water like that before. I'd heard about stone tools being discovered on Flores, but I hadn't thought that much of it." (The Wallace Line is a biogeographical term referring to a hypothetical boundary in the distribution of fauna. It's named after naturalist Alfred Russel Wallace, who proposed it. Wallace is also credited as co-discoverer, with Charles Darwin, of the theory of evolution by natural selection.)

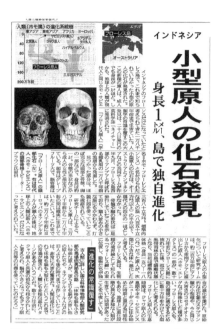

Fig. 4-2: A Japanese newspaper article on the *H. floresiensis* find.
Headline: "Tiny early human fossil found in Indonesia. One meter tall. Unique evolutionary path on island."

The Wallace Line extends from the Lombok Strait separating the islands of Bali and Lombok north through the Makassar Strait between the islands of Borneo and Sulawesi. Biota in the region west of the line is closer to that of the Asian continent ("Oriental region"), while biota to the east is closer to that of Australia ("Australian region"). When sea levels fell during the Ice Age, previously submerged lands west of the Wallace Line were exposed, forming a land bridge with the Asian continent called Sundaland. Exposed landforms to the east of the Wallace Line merged with Australia and New Guinea to form the Sahul continent. The standard explanation is that biotas of the two regions at the time are still reflected to the present day. Strictly speaking, the islands of East Indonesia have a different biota than Australia and New Guinea. The conceptual boundary between these two regions is known as Lydekker's Line. Our concern is with the Wallace Line.

Even by the oldest estimates, *Homo erectus* reached Asia about one million and several hundred thousand years ago. After that time, even if

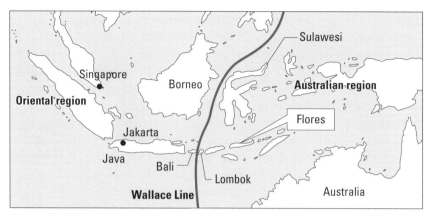

Fig. 4-3: The Wallace Line.

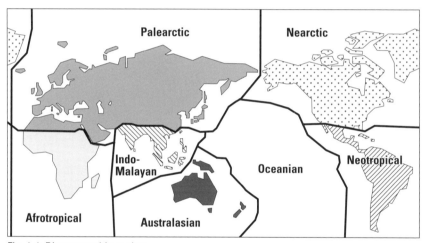

Fig. 4-4: Biogeographic realms.

there had been a land bridge as far as Bali or Borneo, it would still have been necessary to cross open ocean water in some fashion to travel farther east than the Lombok or Makassar Straits. The conventional wisdom was that *H. sapiens* were the first to accomplish that crossing.

In that case, what did Dr. Kaifu mean by "a totally unexpected human species"? "*H. floresiensis* is very small," he told me, "about a meter tall, exhibiting a dramatic degree of dwarfism. And its brain size slightly exceeds 400 cc (Fig. 1-5), not that different from chimpanzees. If we're to assume they evolved into this dwarfed form from Java Man, the geographically closest human species, their brain size had shrunk by half or more. From the emergence of the genus *Homo* on, human evolution is all about the enlargement of the body and the expansion of the brain, but this goes in the completely opposite direction. "The small brain is a particular problem, given that a relatively big brain is part of the definition of genus *Homo*. Now that definition will have to be changed."

Flores Man had a small body and small brain. In the 2004 paper, their brain size was estimated to be a mere 380 cc, making it smaller than that of larger chimpanzees. Subsequent research by Dr. Kubo of Hokkaido University and Dr. Kaifu led to this estimate being revised upward to 426 cc. However, it's quite small even after this adjustment.

Despite being such a rule-breaking entity in terms of human evolution, effectively defying the definition of the genus, *H. floresiensis* must be considered genus *Homo* based on other characteristics. Clearly, they are humans who challenge the imagination.

Challenging the Definition of Genus *Homo*

What could have brought on these physiological changes?

Putting aside the issue of the thoroughly unexpectedness of the place where Flores Man was discovered, it's possible to provisionally provide a biological explanation for the dwarfism.

"In the isolated environment of an island, a phenomenon known as 'island rule' can take over," Dr. Kaifu explained. "Island rule is a condition when large fauna tend to grow smaller and small fauna tend to grow larger. On Flores, the ancient elephant Stegodon shrank to a shoulder height of only about 1.5 meters, whereas the flightless marabou stork grew to a height of 1.8 meters. It's conceivable, then, that *H. floresiensis* ancestors could have been subject to island rule, too, and shrunk.

"Even so, this is an unaccountable reduction in size. With a brain so small, you have to wonder whether it could even have functioned as a human. Yet it's been established beyond a doubt that they made stone tools. It was shocking to find the physical size of humans could change this much, the same as other animals."

Because this idea of island rule is so important, it's worth elaborating on. In an island environment with limited life resources (habitats, food, etc.), large fauna are prone to dwarfism, shrinking to a size that's advantageous for having a lower metabolism and more rapid reproductive maturation.

Conversely, smaller fauna can tend toward gigantism, as predators are relatively rare on islands and there is less evolutionary pressure to maintain a small form suited for concealment.

In Japan, for instance, it's well-known that formerly large macaques and *sika* deer on Yakushima Island are smaller than their cousins on the main island of Honshu.

These factors lead to the straightforward interpretation that *H. floresiensis* were simply one type of fauna among others living on an isolated island and underwent dwarfism in conformance with island rule. This shouldn't be that surprising if we accept that humans are animals, too. However, when we consider it was genus *Homo* that was affected, a genus that had begun evolving in a distinctly different direction from all other animals, we can see how the small body size, and especially the small brain size, might sow confusion and challenge the very definition of genus *Homo*.

In the Cool Cave

I travelled to Flores in March 2016 to learn a little more about the world in which *H. floresiensis* had lived. Let me begin with Liang Bua Cave, where the first *H. floresiensis* skeleton was discovered.

One way of getting to Flores is to fly into Denpasar International Airport, on Bali, one of the more popular tourist destinations in Indonesia. You then take a domestic flight to Labuanbajo ("Bajo" to locals) in western Flores. When I went, there were two flights daily.

Labuanbajo is also the key departure point for boats to the islands of Komodo and Rinca, where Komodo dragons still live. Although it's only 60 kilometers as the crow flies from Labuanbajo to Liang Bua, the road winds through mountain paths, and the actual trip is well over 100 kilometers and can take three or four hours. The scenery along the way alternates between forest and agricultural landscapes, similar in many respects to Japan.

I finally came to Liang Bua Cave, located in low hills rising from a plain of rice paddies. The entrance was semicircular, some 50 meters in diameter. Beyond that, it was too dark to see. Stalactites hung like icicles from the ceiling. Liang Bua is still the site of an active excavation, sealed off with barbed wire and locked to bar entry. I managed to get the on-site manager to open the passageway and let me in.

Fig. 4-5: Liang Bua Cave.

Entering the cave, I felt the cool, almost chill air and experienced the meaning of Liang Bua, which transltates as "cool cave." And it was big. Once my eyes adjusted to the dark interior, I could tell the cave curved to my left. It looked like it went on for a considerable distance.

"Over here," said the on-site manager, drawing my attention to the floor of the cave along the left-hand wall. Excavation season was over, and the excavation pit had been filled in. Even so, I could see where it had been, as the ground there was clearly softer than the surrounding cave floor. It was a rectangle measuring four by six meters. I understand that by then (March 2016), the research team had already gone down 10 meters or more at the deepest point. The LB1 skeleton was found about six meters down, meaning that digging had continued beyond that. There were ladders for climbing in and out of the pit and wooden boards and lengths of bamboo shoring to prevent earth collapse.

I couldn't help but feel the discoverers' obsession about this excavation. Even if it was known that stone tools were here, it must have taken incredible persistence and physical effort to dig all throughout the cave until ultimately finding a human fossil six meters below the floor.

I felt in my bones there had once been a different human species living in this place. And once I accepted that truth, I was seized by a sense of being somehow linked through the shadowed dimension of this cave to those days so long ago. How had those tiny *H. floresiensis* used this cave? The cave would have been more than sufficient to ward off the intense sunlight, and when night fell they could have slept safely a little further within. Island "dragons" would have been the huge Komodo, which,

Fig. 4-6: LB1 excavation site.

being larger than these humans, would surely have been their natural ene-
mies. However, the cave would have been defensible, since it was open
and without dense vegetation to shield an approach.

Of course, there are dangers inside caves as well as outside. A few
dozen meters in Liang Bua grows dark, narrow, and quite scary. Water
drips, and there are places where deep pits open up in the floor. You can't
see the bottom even if you shine a light down the pits, and if you drop a
stone down one, there's a rather long pause before it hits water below.
Falling into one of these pits would mean death. In fact, the LB1 female
first discovered and such fossils as LB6 (jawbone from a different individual than LB1) were quite well-preserved: both were covered in mud
soon after they died, suggesting they died in the cave.

Finest Specimens of Asian archaic *Homo*

After walking awhile inside the cave, I was guided to the tiny Liang Bua
Museum not five minutes away on foot. As with the cave itself, it has no
set hours; rather, it's open when someone comes around and asks to be let
in. From the outside, the facility looks more like a wood farmhouse with
a thatched roof than a natural history museum. It was built after the discovery of *H. floresiensis* and, when I visited, had only the base of a future
statue of this human in the forecourt.

I found it oddly heartwarming that the exhibits began with a display
panel on Java Man. A panel explained how the first "Out-of-Africa"
migration of humankind had taken place long before *H. sapiens* emerged

in Africa and spread throughout the world. With it was a portrait of Eugène Dubois, the discoverer of Java Man.

There seemed to be an implicit suggestion that among the *H. erectus* who travelled this far from distant Africa, Java Man represented the group that migrated to Java and *H. floresiensis* was their descendant. However, it hadn't then been established scientifically whether *H. floresiensis* was a descendant of Java Man. There were quite detailed exhibits about the excavation work and the many fossils and stone tools that have been found, as one would expect from Liang Bua Cave's own museum.

The first actual excavations at Liang Bua were done in 1965 by Theodor Verhoeven, a Dutch Catholic missionary priest. He initially used the cave as the site for an elementary school and is said to have intuited that some sort of archaeological or anthropological discovery was waiting to be made under the school's floor—the cave floor. When an elementary

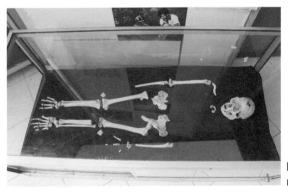

Fig. 4-7: LB1 skeleton replica, Liang Bua museum.

Fig. 4-8: Author looking at the replica.

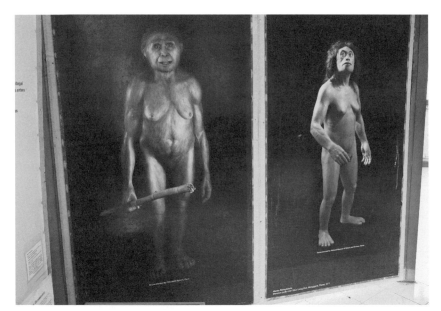

Fig. 4-9: Two representations of LB1.
Roughly full-size depictions showing the Musée de l'Homme model at left and the National Museum model at right.

school was built in town and the children relocated to the new building, Verhoeven began to dig.

However, the place he dug was near the wall on the opposite side of the cave from where *H. floresiensis* would later be discovered. He did find burial site remains and grave goods of Neolithic *H. sapiens*, but he missed Flores Man.

Local researchers subsequently conducted intermittent investigations that yielded primarily Neolithic remains from 3,000 to 2,000 years ago at depths up to three meters. At the turn of the century, an Indonesian-Australian team went deeper, finally encountering *H. floresiensis* six meters down.

I also found familiar faces in some of the photos on display: members of the excavation team working with Dr. Kaifu at the Sambungmacan site. The Indonesian side has often mounted joint investigation teams for excavations in this manner, with researchers welcomed from all over the world.

Of course, the highlight of the museum exhibits is LB1, the key specimen found in the cave. Though a replica, there's something special about this figure lying only some 200 meters from where she had been discovered. I felt like telling her, "I've come all this way to meet you!"

When I got close, I was struck anew by how small she was. Judging from size alone, the replica skeleton laid out in the glass case seemed for all the world to be that of a child. I could understand the story that the excavation team first thought she was a child. It must have been quite a shock when her skeleton proved to be an adult female's.

The team found not only the skull and facial bones but also the entire body, from shoulder blades and pelvic bone to hands and feet. The legs were in particularly good condition, from femurs to toe bones.

As early *Homo* fossils go, the state of preservation of LB1 is among the best in the world. Considering that no full skeleton of Java Man or Peking Man has been found, that decidedly makes this the best premodern *Homo* specimen in Asia, and because of its tiny size, one of the greatest discoveries in archeological history.

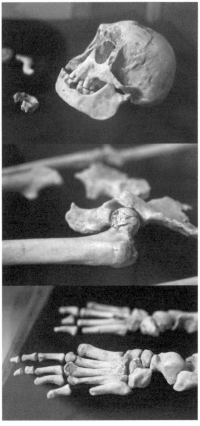

Fig. 4-10: Replica of well-preserved LB1 skeleton bones.
Top: skull, middle: femurs, Bottom: Toes.

World-class paleoartist Elisabeth Dyanès created a life-size figure of her for the Musée de l'Homme in Paris, as did Dr. Kaifu and his colleagues for the National Museum. Although their details differ, both models incorporate the available scientific knowledge. Here at the Liang Bua museum you can see what they look like side-by-side.

Based on the same specimen, the two models give different impressions. The Daynès version seems gentler. The National Museum's, rather feral, holds a stone tool found at the site and is missing its left little toe.

Observing both, I mused about what the lives of *H. floresiensis* would have been like in Liang Bua Cave.

New Species or Diseased Specimen

It was understood that an unexpected human species had been found in an unexpected place. As the discovery confounded all expectations, researchers wondered how to explain it. Naturally, there were opinions at odds with the interpretations presented in the initial paper, and this led to controversy.

"First of all was the question of whether this was really a new human species," Dr. Kaifu said. "There was criticism that this was nothing more than a diseased specimen of *H. sapiens*. Specifically, there were opinions that the small brain was the result of microcephaly, and that the small body could be the product of some sort of growth disorder such as Laron syndrome [Laron-type dwarfism] or a thyroid dysfunction. In fact, the LB1 skull is slightly deformed, asymmetric. Some claimed this proved serious growth disorder."

This was the opinion asserting a new human species had not been discovered. The initial paper estimated that the specimen could be from as recent as 12,000 years ago, a time when modern humans were already inhabiting nearby islands. This would tend to substantiate the malformation argument and did indeed engender support.

Fig. 4-11: Replica of the LB1 skull with its bilateral asymmetry.

Problems of Size and Distance

There was another bone of contention, even for those acknowledging Liang Bua fossils were a new human species: Where had the species originated?

"As a first premise, there are the geographical conditions," Dr. Kaifu said. "At that time, human fossils had only been found on Flores in strata at Liang Bua dating back some tens of thousands of years. So, it hadn't been possible to use fossil evidence to trace the evolutionary trajectory of these specimens through time. There had been reports of stone tools dating between one million and 700,000 years ago on Flores, at a site in the So'a Basin, establishing beyond a reasonable doubt that primitive humans had indeed reached Flores by that time. As it seemed unlikely that such humans had traveled to this isolated island multiple times, it appeared probable that the makers of the stone tools from the So'a Basin were the ancestors of the human fossils found in Liang Bua."

The 2016 So'a Basin discovery was a significant new development. I've been there and will go into further detail about that journey later. For now, let me focus on the controversy that ensued following the discovery of *H. floresiensis:* Did she in fact represent a new human species?

Compared to the vast African continent, Flores had once been viewed as merely an island beyond easy reach. Even during the Ice Age, when the sea level was at its lowest, the Lombok Strait between Bali and Lombok was still some 20 kilometers across, and the current was probably fast. And even if a human managed to cross that first strait, there would have been more ocean crossings of several kilometers at a stretch before finally arriving at Flores.

The difficulty in making these journeys is clear from the lack of animals traveling from the Asian continent to Flores. The only mammals on the island at the time were rodents and Stegodon elephants. The belief is that rodents drifted there from Asia and that Stegodons were powerful, proficient swimmers. Primates as a rule are not at their best in water. Until this discovery, it had been taken for granted that this characteristic was only overcome after the emergence of *H. sapiens* and their acquisition of rudimentary ocean navigation skills.

Now, however, the accumulating evidence of fossils and stone tools is leading to the belief that *H. floresiensis's* ancestors had reached Flores by some means at least a million years ago and underwent dwarfism on the island. Who was it, then, who reached the island and became so small?

"There are two scenarios," Dr. Kaifu said. "One is that the large and geographically proximate Java Man came to Flores and underwent dwarfism. The other is that *H. floresiensis* evolved directly from a human species that was more primitive than Java Man and had a small body and a small brain."

For present purposes, let's say Hypothesis A refers to geographically nearby Java Man shrinking and Hypothesis B to *H. floresiensis* evolving directly from a more primitive and smaller human species. Pros and cons of each are noted in Fig. 4-12.

As for Hypothesis A, Dr. Kaifu said, "If they evolved from Java Man,

	Hypothesis	Pros	Cons
A	Dwarfed from Java Man	Geographic proximity	Too severe dwarfism • Height reduced by 30% or more • Brain size reduced by half or more
B	Evolved from smaller, more primitive hominin	Less severe dwarfism	No evidence for such primitive hominins in Asia

Fig. 4-12: Pros and cons of Hypotheses A and B.

they certainly would have been in geographical proximity, but Java Man would have been a bit too big. They were as tall as 1.6 to 1.7 meters. To shrink from that to a height of 1.1 meters would be extreme, and moreover, the brain would have shrunk by half or more. Many researchers think such shrinkage is too dramatic."

Brain size reduction by half or more surely indicates severe dwarfism. Since such shrinkage would call into question the identity of humankind, as well as the very definition of genus *Homo*, it's only natural that many researchers were concerned if not confounded.

What, then, of Hypothesis B? "If it turns out that *H. floresiensis* evolved in a direct lineage from a smaller and more primitive human species than Java Man, such as *H. habilis* in Africa two million years ago, then the degree of dwarfism would be a bit less severe," Dr. Kaifu explained. "At present, there's no evidence that such primitive early species of genus *Homo* made it to Asia." Both hypotheses having flaws, the debate continues.

A Surprise Invitation

Dr. Kaifu joined the research team and has been working since 2007 to untangle the various threads of the debate. It all began with a request for Dr. Kaifu and Dr. Baba to generate descriptions of *H. floresiensis* skulls and teeth. We've already seen Dr. Kaifu's research into Java Man's teeth and skulls in Chapter 3. His attention to detail won acclaim from other researchers and led to his being called on to assist the Indonesian-Australian research team with the *H. floresiensis* excavation site.

Although an Indonesian-Australian team had already published a paper on the discovery of *H. floresiensis* (*Nature* 431, 1055–1061 (2004)), as previously mentioned, newly discovered life forms are not formally recognized until description papers are published with detailed descriptions of the characteristics of the new discovery based upon the specimen found. And because the detailed research needed for such work takes time, it is common with human fossils of interest to first publish an initial description and then prepare a detailed description. *H. floresiensis* was no exception.

In this instance, the 2004 paper published in *Nature* was an initial report, with the detailed description papers published in the *Journal of Human Evolution* (*JHE*) and other publications in 2009. There were several papers published collectively on the holotype specimen LB1 jaw, on the comparison with the LB6/1 jaw discovered later, and on LB1's upper and lower limbs. Research on the shoulder bones was published later. Individual descriptions were made of different parts of the specimen thanks to its good condition.

Dr. Kaifu joined the project after it was well underway, and his paper on the LB1 skull and teeth was published in 2011, also in the *JHE*. Since then, he has written numerous papers on *H. floresiensis* in addition to his continuing work on Java Man, and it is worth noting that he also published his findings on a Sangiran skull (skull IX) in the same issue of the *JHE* as his paper on LB1. Indeed, I suspect there was a synergetic effect from the fact that he was working with both at the same time.

Child, Disease, or Island Rule

How, then, do we unravel the controversy surrounding the human fossils from Flores?

As a warm-up exercise, we begin with the possibility—that any of us might think of—that the small human specimen LB1 was an *H. sapiens* child. This is plausible, considering the anecdote about how the team who first made the discovery initially thought the bones were those of a child. Dr. Kaifu, however, promptly and decisively refuted this argument. "There was nothing that said child," he said, "The teeth are all grown in." That settles that. On this point, there is no room for doubt. LB1 is an adult.

What, then, about the diseased *H. sapiens* hypothesis? This is the idea that the specimen was an adult *H. sapiens* who was unusually small due to some sort of growth disorder. If true, this would be the simplest way to end the debate. At least there'd be no concern about the origin of *H. floresiensis*, and it would be possible to treat the dwarfism as a disorder rather than the result of island rule or some other phenomenon. Such a conclusion may not advance paleoanthropology, but it might end the controversy. So, which aspects of the competing hypotheses have been debated? "Conditions such as microcephaly, Laron syndrome, or thyroid dysfunction have all been suggested," Dr. Kaifu said. "However, there are still no papers that clearly indicate modern humans assume a morphology like LB1's due to such conditions. Conversely, researchers from the United States and Australia have indicated that, rather than thinking in terms of it being a disease, there are, in fact, characteristics of *H. floresiensis* similar to *Homo erectus* or other primitive forms of *Homo*."

"Look at this," Dr. Kaifu said, handing me a replica of LB1 made with data from a micro-CT scan and output from a high-precision 3D printer when he was writing his description paper. At first, I was uncertain whether I should hold it but then felt more comfortable and was finally able to study it.

"Do you remember the characteristics of *Homo erectus*?" Dr. Kaifu asked me. "You see how the face is inclined and protruding forward. And it's got slight supraorbital ridges. This skull is completely unlike *H. sapiens*. And the head height is completely different, too. It's obvious when you put it alongside a modern human skull." Dr. Kaifu placed the replica next to a specimen of a modern human that he had in his laboratory. This was of an East Indian. Modern humans (*H. sapiens*) have rounded, high skulls; clean-cut, flat faces; rounded occiputs; and projecting jaws with chins. In contrast, LB1 has a low skull, protruding face, strongly flexed occiput, and no chin.

Even I could tell all of this at a glance. If you think back to our earlier discussions about Java Man, then you're likely to see the characteristics just listed for LB1 are almost the same as those we were told are characteristic of that species.

No *H. sapiens* disease that may have caused such distinct character-

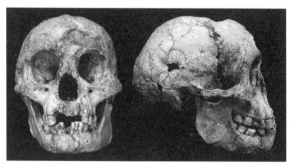

Fig. 4-13: LB1 skull.

istics has been proposed to date. Instead, when examined by researchers experienced with early *Homo* fossils, the question becomes, "What else could LB1 be except an early *Homo*?"

Definitive Argument Against Growth Disorder

The best way to convince formidable disputants is to carefully answer every question they lob at you. Some researchers suggest the LB1 skull asymmetry supports the hypothesis that LB1 was the product of a growth disorder. The LB1 skull is bilaterally asymmetric, deformed; in short, the LB1 person had been diseased and her growth impaired.

Dr. Kaifu published a paper that clearly refutes this argument. "I showed LB1 to a specialist at the National Center for Child Health and Development in Japan," he explained, "and was told it was a case of deformational plagiocephaly. That's when a baby's head deforms in line with how they're laid down, as their skulls are soft. It still happens today and is familiar to doctors. But it doesn't cause growth disorder. Therefore, there's no need to assume that a deformation in LB1 means a growth disorder. Furthermore, the LB1 skull and little toe show signs of having been injured and having healed. This suggests she wasn't an invalid but got around quite actively."

A little checking reveals that deformational plagiocephaly, or positional plagiocephaly, occurs frequently even today. Having the back of the head flat rather than rounded—please note this is not the approved medical jargon—is also known as a type of deformational plagiocephaly. While there is a hypothesis that gross deformation is a risk factor for a slight delay in neurodevelopment and motor development, it would not be the cause of a growth failure resulting in a person who grew no taller than one meter.

All of which clearly refutes the hypothesis for *H. floresiensis* as a diseased *H. sapiens*. The counterargument can be easily made that LB1 is morphologically similar to early *Homo*, with the significant asymmetry in the skull explainable as a common phenomenon rather than a growth disorder.

However, it seems some people are never satisfied. "Some people just keep digging in their heels. It's really something else," said Dr. Kaifu. It will probably take still more time to finally resolve the various arguments, now that they have gotten out into the world.

Let me add that it's been suggested the *H. floresiensis* ancestor was neither a diseased *Homo sapiens* nor another *erectus*-grade *Homo* but an even more ancient, small-bodied early hominin. In Dr. Kaifu's judgment, however, there are no elements of *Australopithecus* in the characteristics of LB1: the face is not as large, nor are jaw or teeth extremely large with respect to the head. Accordingly, Dr. Kaifu concluded that it is appropriate to classify LB1 as part of genus *Homo* rather than *Australopithecus*.

Nonetheless, the introduction into the debate of all manner of hominins—*Australopithecus* to modern humans—as the possible identity of a single set of fossils shows how this specimen is the exemplar of "a totally unexpected human species." Thus, we are left with a provisional "most likely hypothesis," namely, that early *Homo* of Flores is the descendant of one or another early *Homo* group that arrived on the island about one million years ago.

With that established, we must envision a scenario in which they rapidly became significantly smaller in the island environment. And this brings us to the next question: What kind of early *Homo* was the ancestor of *H. floresiensis*?

Hypothesis A states that Java Man, in geographical proximity but larger in size, is the ancestor of *H. floresiensis*. Hypothesis B conjectures that *H. habilis*, somewhat small-bodied but geographically and temporally distant, is that ancestor.

Both are early members of genus *Homo*, the human genus. In that sense, *Homo floresiensis* is indeed an appropriate name.

"The initial *Nature* paper was written to suggest that *H. floresiensis* most likely evolved from Java Man," said Dr. Kaifu. "But the debate holding that body size and brain size alike had been reduced too far to have come from Java Man arose immediately thereafter, and even the paper's authors began to say it was possible that *H. floresiensis* had descended from a group with small bodies and small brains, such as

Java Man   *H. floresiensis*

Fig. 4-14: Body sizes of Java Man and *Homo floresiensis*.

H. habilis or even an *Australopithecus* which had been in Africa at an even earlier time. If these had been their ancestors, then the degree of dwarfism would not have been quite so severe."

What, then, was Dr. Kaifu's view? What conclusions did he draw from getting face-to-face with the specimen for long periods of time, almost as though having conversations with it, to write his description of the LB1 skull?

Which Human Shrank?

The LB1 skull is a delicate little thing, small enough that it seems you could hold it in the palm of your hand. I was shocked by the size when I held it. Experts are as sensitive to shape as to size, and they think in terms of which human species would have a morphologically similar skull.

"At first glance, I thought the *H. floresiensis* skull was closer to that of Java Man," said Dr. Kaifu. "I had a decisive advantage in having seen all the Java fossils and having data on them. I was researching Java Man and viewing fossils from Africa while others had been looking only at Africa without having considered Java Man. I think that led them in the wrong direction."

This seemed to be researcher intuition at play, so I asked Dr. Kaifu to elaborate. Might there be a specific example that anyone would easily understand on sight?

"To take an example, the *H. habilis* characteristics include large teeth, a robust jaw, and a large skull base," Dr. Kaifu explained. "While this hasn't received that much recognition, these elements are some of the primary characteristics of early *Homo* from around two million years ago. The jaw and the base of the skull above it are large, and yet the brain itself is comparatively tiny. It's a bell shape, with a wide base and a narrow head atop it.

"Contrast this with later groups of early *Homo*, for whom the jaw gets smaller, the cranial vault gets narrower, and the temporal cranial walls— the skull's side walls—stand up straighter, while the head itself becomes more rounded.

"In this regard, LB1 is closer to *H. erectus*, and especially to early Java Man, than to *H. habilis*. Leaving aside absolute sizes, the overall shapes and proportions overwhelmingly point to it."

Given the relationship between the shape of the head and the shape of the brain cavity, this is a matter intrinsic to human evolution. The thing to keep in mind is that the shape of the head is the significant determiner in deciding which is correct—that *H. floresiensis* was an early *Homo* and not *H. sapiens* or that *H. floresiensis* was closer to *H. erectus* than to *H. habilis*. While it had been possible prior to LB1 to describe a scenario in which the human head became larger and rounder and brain size increased, the rather

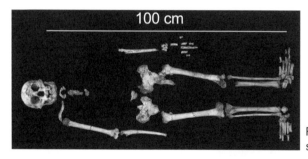

Fig. 4-15: Remarkably small LB1 skeleton.

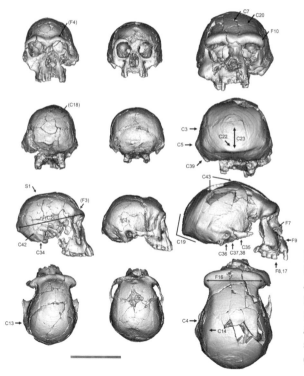

Fig. 4-16: Comparison of LB1 with *H. habilis* and Java Man (*H. erectus*). LB1 is at center, *H. habilis* on left, Java Man on right. Arrows indicate points of similarity between LB1 and the other two specimens.

intrusive arrival of this peculiar new entity whose brain size had shrunk—even as it retained a similar silhouette—had opened up the debate.

While Dr. Kaifu explained the matter in general terms, his 2011 description paper identified nearly 70 skull characteristics with comparative examination. This involved the same process as in his previously discussed comparison paper on Java Man skulls. In the paper, the *H. floresiensis* specimen is compared to such species as *H. habilis*, African *H. erectus*, Dmanisi Man from Georgia, early- and late-period Javan *H. erectus* (Java Man), *H. erectus* from China (Peking Man), and late archaic *Homo* who emerged in China after *Homo erectus*.

While these examinations are beyond the scope of this book, we can perhaps get some appreciation of the situation by looking at Fig. 4-16 comparing *H. habilis* (a renowned specimen known as KNM-ER 1813), *H. floresiensis* (LB1), and an early *H. erectus* (Java Man Sangiran 17).

Scenario: Early Java Man Evolved

The results indicated that while there were points of similarity between *H. habilis* and LB1, they were few in number. Conversely, there were nearly 20 indicators showing a resemblance between early Java Man and LB1. The following conclusion was therefore reached.

"We conclude that the craniofacial morphology of LB1 is consistent with the hypothesis that *H. floresiensis* evolved from early Javanese *H. erectus* with dramatic island dwarfism."

The phrasing is cautious, as befits a scientific paper. Nonetheless, Dr. Kaifu has clearly pointed out that the scenario of *H. floresiensis* having evolved from Java Man, and from early Java Man at that, follows naturally from the skull morphologies.

What detracts from this hypothesis is that it requires brain size to have shrunk by half or even more. Brain growth is crucial to the definition of genus *Homo*, and by extension, of the theory of human evolution to date. This is why some researchers found it difficult to accept that brain size could have shrunk so much. It also explains why the opinion that the ancestor of *H. floresiensis* was small early *Homo* such as *H. habilis* remained unshaken even after publication of Dr. Kaifu's paper. In response, Dr. Kaifu did additional research to further substantiate both his intuition and corroborative evidence found while preparing his description paper.

Accurate Measurements of Brain Size

Dr. Kaifu asked, "If Java Man was LB1's ancestor, would LB1 really have shrunk to this extent?" Could the numbers that crunched the scenario for transition from Java Man to *H. floresiensis* have been off to begin with? And was this what had made the hypothesis for Java Man as ancestor seem so difficult to accept?

Numbers crunched concerned:

> ➤ Brain size of *H. floresiensis* (LB1)
> ➤ Brain size of Java Man
> ➤ Relation between human body & brain sizes (change curve in brain size)

In a 2013 paper, Dr. Kaifu examined all three points. "If I may explain by starting with the first point," Dr. Kaifu told me, "Dr. Kubo, then a post-doc at the University of Tokyo, accurately assayed the LB1 brain size using high-precision CT data. When the Australian team members made their initial report, LB1 was in an inadequate state of cleaning and restoration, and they measured the inside of the head using the classical method of filling it with what they said were mustard seeds. This gave them a result of 380 cc. Other researchers carried out some cleaning of the specimen and arrived at a figure of 430 cc, while yet others performed CT scans and concluded it was 400 cc. All kinds of numbers were being thrown around."

The method employed by Dr. Kaifu and his associates was more appropriate to the 2010s. "Using the image data obtained with a precision CT scan of LB1, Dr. Kubo carefully 'cleaned' the interior of the skull on the computer," Dr. Kaifu explained. "Then he also virtually reconstructed portions that had been damaged, doing so one by one and taking considerable time. The number he derived was 426 cc. This was a high-precision finding with an accuracy of plus or minus 3 cc, which it is fair to call definitive. Thus, the figure of 380 cc given in the 2004 paper was understated—it's a bit larger. That was our first finding, which related to point number one." The figure of 380 cc, most commonly cited before as the brain size of *H. floresiensis*, had now been revised upward. It was an increase of over 10 percent, an amount not to be taken lightly.

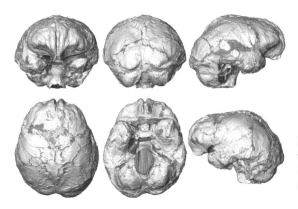

Fig. 4-17: Computer-based virtual endocranial cast of LB1 created by Dr. Kubo and associates.

Rethinking Java Man's Brain Size

Let us now consider the second point, the brain size of Java Man. "What I found out from my research in 2011 was that the earliest-period Java Man is the one whom *H. floresiensis* most resembles," said Dr. Kaifu. "In other words, it conforms to a scenario in which an ancient iteration of Java Man came to Flores and thereafter followed a unique evolutionary path there over the course of a million years or so. However, the number used thus far for initial brain size in the scenario in which *H. floresiensis* underwent dwarfism from *H. erectus* was 991 cc, an overall average derived from the brain sizes of *H. erectus* from Africa, China, and Asia across various periods. No matter how you look at it, this is ridiculous."

Recall that Dr. Kaifu's earlier research demonstrated that Java Man had evolved over time. Shrinkage of the masticatory apparatus and enlargement of brain size are trends seen in the evolution of genus *Homo* overall, and Java Man has shown the same changes, despite having been believed to have gone virtually unchanged for ages on Java.

"Given that my associates and I believe *H. floresiensis's* ancestors were probably an ancient type of Java Man," said Dr. Kaifu, "it's appropriate to turn to early-period Java Man for brain size, rather than take an average of specimens from various eras. The brain size then was on the order of 860 cc."

The number used for comparing the brain sizes of *H. erectus* and *H. floresiensis* drops from 991 to 860 cc—a 13 percent reduction.

"So, the ancestor value is reduced a little, while the descendant value increases a little," continued Dr. Kaifu. "That shrinks the gap somewhat. This was our second finding."

Previous thinking had been 380 vs. 991 cc, or 38.3 percent. Brain size in *H. floresiensis* would have had to shrink to less than 40 percent of the ancestral size! The 426 vs. 860 cc values that Dr. Kaifu considered, however, require a reduction to 49.5 percent instead, or approximately half. This is still, however, a significant difference.

Relation of Body Size to Brain Size

The third point examined in the paper is the relationship between body size and brain size in humans (the change curve in brain size). And this is where matters get a bit complicated.

It's believed *H. floresiensis* became smaller in conformance with the island rule in the isolated environment of Flores. Yet that is still an extreme case. If it had just been the body that shrunk, it might have been plausible, but the reduction in brain size seemed unbelievable. This is the point emphasized by Dr. Robert D. Martin, provost and curator of the Biological Anthropology Department at Chicago's Field Museum and an expert in primate anatomy and brain evolution. His 2006 paper in *Science* magazine says the LB1 specimen was a microcephalic *Homo sapiens*.

The crux of the argument is allometry. "Allo-" is the prefix for "different" or "other;" "-metry" means "measure" or "measurement." In short, it refers to relative growth and describes the relation between measurements of two different parts of an organism. As this explanation alone is probably not clear enough, let me write out the equation: $Y=bX^{\alpha}$ where Y is the *Homo sapiens* brain capacity, bX is body mass, and α is the relational coefficient.

It appears simple enough. In fact, it swings past simple to seeming almost frighteningly casual. But it's profoundly significant. If these were mere straightforward proportional relations, then the linear equation $Y=bX$ would suffice to describe them, and α would always be 1. In fact, however, the equation signifies that these are not straightforward proportional relations and α is not always 1.

According to Dr. Martin, when Y is the brain size of *H. sapiens* and bX is overall mass, then α ranges from 0.03 to 0.17. Since α is much smaller than 1, brain size does not decrease that much, even when overall mass decreases. If we hypothesize this equation is applicable to genus *Homo* generally, then the evolution of the *H. floresiensis* brain from the *H. erec-*

tus (the species that includes Java Man) brain would have entailed an inconceivable degree of reduction in body size as well.

"How much should overall body mass have decreased for *H. erectus*, with a mean brain size of 991 cc and overall mass of 60 kilograms, to reach the *H. floresiensis* brain size of 400 cc?" Dr. Kaifu asked rhetorically. "Plugging these values into the allometric equation, we get something on the order of 0.3 kilograms or less. This is unrealistic, no matter how you look at it. Consider that the overall mass of LB1 is estimated from its bone morphology to be 16 to 29 kilograms. Dr. Martin's argument was that if *H. erectus* was to have shrunk into *H. floresiensis,* the problem of mass could not be explained, and therefore the only conceivable conclusion was that the brain of LB1 was small due to a pathological impairment. In other words, he asserted there was a high probability *H. floresiensis* was actually a microcephalic *H. sapiens.*"

This opinion carried considerable weight, as it was published by such a known authority in a leading scientific journal. During discussions with Dr. Kubo, Dr. Kaifu wondered whether Dr. Martin's assumptions might not be a little off the mark.

"Exponents used for *H. sapiens* of 0.03 to 0.17 kilograms had been estimated from a sample of a single group of modern humans, the Danes," said Dr. Kaifu. "If you think about it, we've no way of knowing whether those indices accurately represent a trend for all humankind."

To answer this question, Dr. Kubo investigated the relationship between endocranial volume (volume of the skull interior) and overall body size in 20 different populations throughout the world, with reference to various sources and his own measurement data.

"Our thinking was that in order to understand trends in *H. sapiens,* we needed to look at more than the trends within one specific group—we needed to look at trends among a variety of *H. sapiens* groups with different body sizes," explained Dr. Kaifu. "For body size, we substituted femoral head diameter, which is believed to correlate closely with overall body size. Think of it more simply as the size of the hip joint, which bears the weight of the upper body. We wondered what would happen if we plotted the mean values for each group by gender to determine the values for α, and applied those to the gap between early Java Man and LB1."

The *H. sapiens* data used in this instance were gathered evenly from Asia, Australia, Polynesia, North America, Europe, and Africa. Diverse groups were included, ranging from European groups with large body sizes to pygmies. Dr. Kubo and Dr. Kaifu plotted these on a graph and derived new values for α that differed from the exponents estimated from the solely Danish samples. While the variable for body mass was different from what Dr. Martin used in his research, precluding a direct comparison of these newly obtained values with the values in that earlier paper, the results of the study nonetheless showed a stronger correlation between body mass and brain size in *H. sapiens* than was indicated in his paper. In other words, a decrease in body mass would be accompanied by a considerable reduction in brain size.

Applying this relationship to the difference between early Java Man and LB1 clearly indicated that Dr. Martin's estimate had been an outlier. Let's look at a graph (Fig. 4-18) with femoral head diameter on the x-axis and endocranial volume on the y-axis. Note that in both instances we are taking the logarithm. One aspect of the allometric equation that makes it so easy to work with is that, by taking the logarithms on both the x-axis and y-axis, the plot can be rendered as a straight line with the exponent α as its slope.

We plot the data on *H. sapiens* gathered by Dr. Kubo in this coordinate plane, with white circles denoting values for males and black circles denoting values for females, then determine the gender-specific slopes, with dotted lines indicating the slope for males and solid lines indicating that for females. Both lines are slanted to some degree.

Next, let's see what happens if we apply these slopes to early Java Man and *Homo habilis*. Specifically, we extend the lines from the positions of Java Man and *H. habilis* in the coordinate plane in the direction of smaller body mass (or more accurately, smaller femoral head diameter) on the x-axis. When we do so, we see that brain size gets smaller as well. Note that the femoral head diameters used here for early Java Man are estimates ranging between 45 to 50 mm, so Java Man's value is not plotted as a single point but instead as a dotted line representing the possible range.

And what are our results? First, regarding *H. habilis*, we see a near-perfect demonstration of the possibility that if *H. habilis* had shrunk to LB1 size, its brain size would also have shrunk to LB1 size. While this factoid taken by itself might seem to reinforce the *H. habilis* hypothesis, note that the shrinkage from early Java Man also more naturally approaches LB1 in this model than it did in previous hypotheses.

Dr. Kaifu's conclusion stated it's possible to demonstrate that as the body got smaller so did the brain, and this would account for nearly 100 percent of the reduction in brain size for *H. habilis* and around 75 percent

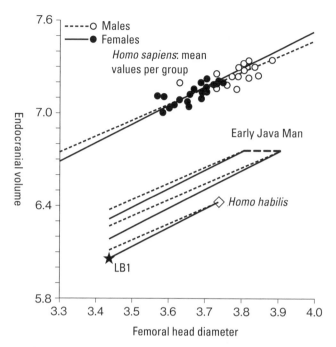

Fig. 4-18: Relationship between body size and brain size.
Predictions of endocranial volume when femoral head diameters (proxy for body size) of early Java Man and *Homo habilis* are reduced to LB1 values.

for early Java Man, or a range of between 50 and 100 percent.

In other words, under the early Java Man hypothesis that Dr. Kaifu endorses based on morphological similarities he found in the skulls and teeth, it's conceivable that in addition to overall body size reduction there would also have been an additional 25 percent reduction in brain size in the case of *H. floresiensis*. Dr. Kaifu and his associates have written a paper stating that such a reduction is entirely plausible, as there have also been reports of greater brain size reduction than would have been predicted from body size occurring in mammals that moved into island habitats.

At a minimum, these findings dealt a significant blow to the hypothesis that *H. floresiensis* was a diseased specimen. While the Java Man ancestor hypothesis may not have been strengthened, the findings indicate that it has not deserved the harshest criticisms leveled at it.

By untangling the issues that had left him uncomfortable one by one, Dr. Kaifu was able to steadily shore up his evidence. In 2015, he also finished his paper on the morphology of LB1 teeth. In this paper, he clarified as well that characteristics of LB1 teeth are close to those of early Java Man.

Puzzling Teeth

When it comes to research on LB1, it seems there's no end to surprises.

Concerning LB1 teeth, Dr. Kaifu has discovered that, while there are similarities to Java Man's teeth, they also display many more modern features, that is, features like the teeth of *H. sapiens*.

To elaborate, the more primitive characteristics of LB1 teeth (those similar to Java Man) are found in the canines and the premolars, while the more progressive characteristics (those more similar to modern humans) are found in the molars. However, there were no aspects shared exclusively with the primitive *H. habilis*, that posited progenitor so perennially taken up in this controversy. This finding further increases the probability that *H. floresiensis* evolved from early Java Man, especially when seen in tandem with our prior analysis of the cranium.

It would be beyond the scope of this book to provide a detailed treatment of all of the aspects of *H. floresiensis* teeth that appear similar to those in modern humans, but one that is comparatively easy to understand is the way LB1 lower molar cusps have become simplified, reduced in number from five to four.

Cusps are the protrusions on the crowns of teeth. Lower molars in humans typically have five primary cusps. However, the second molars in at least half of all of us today have only four cusps. Try touching your own molars with your finger and see how many of these protrusions you have. I seem to have four myself.

In case you're wondering why I am writing about this subject here, please rest assured: the time will come when this knowledge proves most useful.

I should also add that, in conducting this comparative examination, Dr. Kaifu made full use of his set of nearly 500 casts of modern human teeth, which he'd personally collected, and his set of Java Man specimens in his laboratory.

This, then, is a rough synopsis of the research Dr. Kaifu performed after being asked to write his paper on the skull of *H. floresiensis*. However,

I should caution that the controversy still continues, and Dr. Kaifu's paper is by no means the last word on the subject. The debate at present stands as follows: The odds are now running against the diseased *H. sapiens* hypothesis, and the scope of likely alternative hypotheses has been narrowed to the early Java Man origin hypothesis vs. the *H. habilis* origin hypothesis.

In June 2017, a Brazilian researcher and an Italian researcher jointly investigated the relationship between body size and brain size in *H. floresiensis*, building island-rule computer models and running simulations on them. Their conclusion supported the early Java Man origin hypothesis championed by Dr. Kaifu, and a paper on the subject was published in the renowned *Proceedings of the Royal Society of London B: Biological Sciences*. Thus does the debate grow more sophisticated, and it's highly likely the day will come when consensus is finally reached.

"The most important point is: Is it truly possible for humankind to have shrunk to such an extent?" emphasizes Dr. Kaifu. "Did it actually happen? Did early Java Man evolve, as I believe, or did African *H. habilis* reach Asia, or was there some as yet unknown primitive human species involved? I have the idea that we still don't truly understand human evolution in Asia, and the debate on *H. floresiensis* is going to be interesting however it turns out. Wherever the truth may lie, this is the kind of discovery that rewrites textbooks."

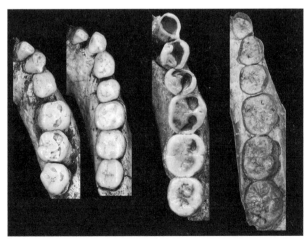

Homo floresiensis   Early Java Man   *Homo habilis*   Fig. 4-19: Lower jaw comparisons with LB1.

Indeed, who can tell what conclusions will be drawn? Will we ever reach a point where we can say we finally have the answer? While Dr. Kaifu continues to gradually shore up his own hypothesis, it seems there's still something missing for it to be regarded as definitive.

"In the final analysis, I don't think the question can ever be definitively resolved with the currently available specimens, no matter how much research we do on them," Dr. Kaifu says. "I'd say the best thing would be to find, somewhere on Flores, fossils of the ancestors of the Liang Bua *H. floresiensis*.

"It's either there or in the So'a Basin, where even more ancient stone tools have been discovered. I'm part of that investigative team, and we're making progress there. Any new developments on that front will get us closer to a resolution."

When I heard this, it became clear that this business of waiting for fossil discoveries that no one can foresee requires taking the long view. I felt keenly how much an excavation is a gamble. It's no easy business to find human fossils from hundreds of thousands of years ago with any certainty. However, when Dr. Kaifu said this, I noticed his expression: serious yet also suddenly showing that distinctive hint of a smile hid somewhere behind his eyes. In fact, as I now reflect on that scene, I realize he already knew about a certain new development from the So'a Basin team.

CHAPTER 5

Big News from the Basin

Something's in the Air

"There's been a new development," Dr. Kaifu told me. I hadn't heard anything, but I hesitated to ask what it was about because the discovery of any human fossil draws tremendous attention. The details aren't openly discussed until published in an academic paper or some other media. Maintaining strict confidentiality is imperative when the discovery is groundbreaking.

It was March 2016, just before my departure for Indonesia to report on the So'a Basin site on Flores Island. Dr. Kaifu gave me the cryptic news as background information for my trip. Many stone tools, the oldest more than a million years old, had been found there. It would come as no surprise if fossils of the toolmakers were also found. If such evidence came to light, we might finally learn the origins of *H. floresiensis*, an event sure to cause a sensation. In the end, that new development would be announced three months later in *Nature*. Before turning to that moment, however, let me tell you what I saw at So'a Basin.

Flores is near the eastern tip of the Sunda Islands. Although not as large

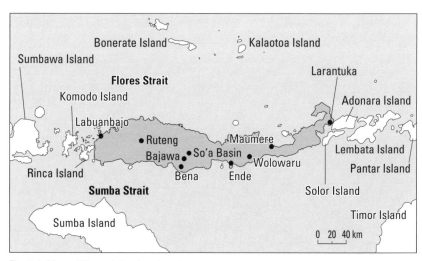

Fig. 5-1: Map of Flores Island and environs.

Fig. 5-2: Mata Menge site, So'a Basin, site of *H. floresiensis*-like fossils dating back 700,000 years. Trench E-32 is under the tent in the foreground.

as Sumatra, Java, or Borneo, Flores is still a substantial island. It runs 350 kilometers east to west, equal to the distance between Tokyo and Nagoya, and has a surface area of 13,500 square kilometers. Compared to places in Japan, it's smaller than Shikoku but bigger than Okinawa. Seen on the map, it may seem eclipsed by Sulawesi or Timor, but setting foot on Flores feels like you're on a big island.

Liang Bua, where *H. floresiensis* was first discovered, is located near the westernmost tip, and So'a Basin is in the middle of the island. The nearest major city is Bajawa. As the crow flies, the distance between Liang Bua and the So'a Basin is no more than 70 to 80 kilometers. But since I am not a crow and the roads are bad, I took a commercial flight, returning first to Labuanbajo and then flying in to Bajawa.

The view from the airplane window was a vista of islands floating in an emerald green ocean. It reminded me of the Earthsea island chain in the novel *A Wizard of Earthsea* by award-winning science fiction and fantasy writer Ursula K. LeGuin. Especially memorable was the lush basin ringed by volcanoes coming into view as we approached the airport from the sea.

The base camp for the Indonesian-Australian team (the Australian side primarily from the University of Wollongong in New South Wales) was the village of Menge Ruda, a 20-minute drive from the airport. From there to the Mata Menge excavation site is 40 minutes on foot, a time estimate based on a healthy, springy stride. As I was loaded down with camera gear, however, it took me an hour.

Here, too, the landscape at first glance seemed to be paddies spreading far and wide all around me, bringing Japan to mind once more. The steep slopes hosted paddy terraces as well as areas of managed grassland cut back on a regular basis. The main landscape was a patchwork of grassland with grazing horses and paddies brimming with water. And in the distance stood magnificent peaks: volcanoes. Several had beautiful ridgelines like the curving slopes of Mt. Fuji. Other places that first appeared to be gently sloping horizon lines turned out to be linked passes between low volcanic peaks. It brought home the visceral sense that I was inside a basin. I was told that the area where most people lived was several hundred square kilometers, while land higher up was predominantly grassland and the path to the excavation site involved a long ascent from the village. At last, I heard the familiar echoing ring of hammers striking chisels. It was Mata Menge Trench E-32—a "working" paleontological excavation site laid out before my eyes.

A Stunning Site to See

Part of the slope of the Mata Menge grasslands had been cut away for the open-pit excavation, exposing sediment dating back between 800,000 and 650,000 years. Though blue tarp had been put up to block the intense sun, the site was a hot, muggy place to work.

I recognized familiar faces among the team excavating Trench E-32: Dr. Iwan Kurniawan, who had led the Indonesian side of the Sambung-macan team, and Dr. Erick Setiyabudi, who had studied in Japan and kept the site upbeat. I greeted them both with "Hey! Long time no see!" Site leader was Dr. Ruly Setiawan, a newly minted PhD from the University of Woolongong. All three were affiliated with the Geological Museum of the Centre for Geological Survey in Bandung and had often worked with Dr. Kaifu. Once we finished catching up, it was time to go see the excavation.

I was stunned! Fossils were poking up from the earth everywhere, so many that I couldn't decide what to look at. The ones that stood out most were fossilized elephant bones. No matter how much they might have been affected by island dwarfism on Flores, these Stegodon fossil bones were still a very respectable size. Jacketed in plaster to protect unearthed sections from exposure to the air, there were long tusks and large teeth lying around, as if there were nothing at all unusual about them—and I don't mean tusks and teeth from merely one or two animals.

The remains excavated at Mata Menge are believed to have been

Fig. 5-3: Trench E-32, site of many fossils.　　Fig. 5-4: Dwarf Stegodon tusk protected in plaster.

Fig. 5-5: Stegodon teeth.

Fig.5-6: Teeth from the Flores giant rat, which grew large due to island rule.

washed to their final resting place by flowing water, so almost nothing recovered so far has remained in an articulated state. As a result, it's not possible to accurately count the animals represented. Nonetheless, judging from the tusk total, it may be said with confidence that at least "a number" of elephant fossils have been found.

While it may seem contradictory after what I just wrote about how big the Stegodon fossils at Mata Menge seemed to be, they were small for their species. Earlier we looked at how being smaller with a lower metabolism and shorter reproductive cycle can be survival-advantageous, but I still found it hard to accept that elephants could get so small. Many elephant species were present long ago in Japan, for example. The early elephant genus *Stegolophodon* of about 1.6 million years ago is known to have shrunk considerably after the land bridge between Japan and the

Asian continent was submerged, but even they weren't as tiny as these Flores Island elephants!

However small the Flores Stegodons might have been, they had walked with magnificent tusks extended—surely an impressive if not intimidating sight—despite how "cute" some people may find them today. They would have been key players coloring the dramatic age in which the ancient humans of Flores lived.

Fig.5-7: Komodo dragon tooth.

Could those humans hunt an elephant of this size? We have no direct evidence they could, but they surely would have eaten a dead one if they ran across a fresh carcass, as suggested by the many stone tools found in the same strata as these fossils. "Look! We're finding these, too," said Dr. Setiyabudi, instructing locals working the excavation, "Giant rat teeth. And this is a dragon tooth."

The most striking thing about these rats are their long, thin front teeth; but the fossils on site were rat molars. In general, island rule means smaller mammals, birds, and reptiles grow larger over time, and on Flores even the little rat has grown immense in line with that general principle. To the island's ancient humans, the rats must have made perfect prey. I understand giant rat fossils also turn up frequently at the Liang Bua excavation.

And then there were the dragons. "Dragons" on Flores refers to Komodo dragons. They survive on neighboring Rinca Island and Komodo Island, some as long as three meters. Even island residents and visiting tourists have been injured by these giant lizards who must've posed a serious threat to early humans. Their teeth aren't large—about the size of a human fingertip—but serrated like carnivorous dinosaur and shark teeth, so they do deserve their dragon name.

It Might Be Human!

Dig, and see what turns up. In the heightened atmosphere of the dig, I also took up hammer and chisel. During my time at Sambungmacan, I'd happily gone toe-to-toe with primeval ages, but this time I was at a place where previously excavated Stegodon fossils lay out on the ground around me. It was an altogether different level of tension. No more than 30 minutes after I'd started, there was a disturbance—excited talk leading to serious conversation. I saw Geological Museum researchers and Indonesian college students with the distinct expression of people trying extra hard to conceal their excitement. "It may be a hominin," the ever-friendly Dr. Setiyabudi told me.

Fig. 5-8: Could this be a human tibia?

Did he mean a fossil that could be an ancestor of the *H. floresiensis* from Liang Bua Cave? The specimen that Dr. Kaifu hoped would prove the key to settling once and for all the debate over *H. floresiensis* and improve our understanding of the history of humankind? Could *that* have just emerged from the earth?

The discoveries continued. A frag-

Fig. 5-9: Might this be part of a human skull?

ment the team thought "might be a skull fragment" was unearthed and meticulously protected and stored away as the first find had been. Professional excavators don't let their excitement show. The team fell silent, focused, as they quietly worked on the task at hand.

After the day's work was done and we walked back to base camp, Iwan, Erick, Ruly, and the others pulled out textbooks on human evolution and debated for a time whether they'd found a tibia. Their conclusion? "We have to send an image to Dr. Kaifu and ask him to look at it." As far as the team was concerned, he was the one they trusted to examine fossil bones.

About the tibia and the skull fragment that excited the research team, Dr. Kaifu said, "The specimens cannot be confirmed as human." Disappointing, yes, but that's the name of the game: the discovery of the century doesn't come along every day.

And yet the following was true: by the time I visited Mata Menge, the team had made their "great discovery," written the paper, and was awaiting publication. This was the "new development" Dr. Kaifu had mentioned prior to my leaving for Flores. "It will be coming out soon," the team members told me. "So, if you promise you won't say a word until publication, then you can have a quick look at it." In short, the paper announced that fossil remains of the ancient humans who made the stone tools of the So'a Basin had been found at last.

For a while, I truly suffered, desperate to tell people about this incredible find yet committed to keeping quiet about it. Three months after that, the paper finally came out in *Nature* (*Nature* 534, 245-248 [2016]). And now, at last, I can happily tell you about the fossil "thought to be an ancestor of *H. floresiensis.*"

The Search for Decisive Evidence

June 2016. Some three months after I returned to Japan from my trip to Flores Island, the National Museum put out a press release stating that the paper "Homo floresiensis-like Fossils from the Early Middle Pleistocene of Flores" reported the discovery of human fossils at So'a Basin's Mata Menge. The specimens from at least three individuals included a human adult mandible and six human teeth from a different jaw, four of them permanent and two deciduous (baby). All were excavated in 2014 at Trench E-32, the site I'd visited on Flores, and estimated to be 700,000 years old (between 800,000 and 650,000 years), much older than the estimated age of 100,000 to 60,000 years for the *H. floresiensis* fossils at Liang Bua (including LB1).

The paper's title, however, avoided stating definitively that the newly discovered fossils were *H. floresiensis*. Instead, it described them as being "*Homo floresiensis*-like." As they'd been discovered on an isolated island where no one had even hypothesized ancient human fossils would be found, there clearly was anticipation they'd prove to be from *H. floresiensis* ancestors. As the only fossils found were teeth and a single jawbone, the paper had to take a cautious stance. The lead author was noted as Dr. Gerrit D. van den Bergh, University of Wollongong, lead institution on the dig, followed by Dr. Kaifu, who performed detailed analysis of the fossils.

"What surprised me was that the specimens were already small around 700,000 years ago," Dr. Kaifu told me later. "Far from being the same size as those of the Liang Bua *H. floresiensis*, these were even smaller. However, there was a major problem with the find. While there was no doubt that the teeth were small, the only other part we had was a lower jaw. Moreover, the jaw itself was damaged and had no teeth left, and it may not have come from an adult. If it was a child's mandible, then it would be natural for it to be so small."

Faced with this uncertainty, Dr. Kaifu searched for a decisive piece of evidence to determine the specimen's development stage. There were tooth sockets for three teeth remaining in a damaged state in the fossil jaw. If they were sockets for the first, second, and third molars, then it was an adult's jaw; if a premolar and a first and second molar, then it was from a child whose teeth had not yet fully grown. To resolve this, the team used CT scans to investigate the mandible's interior structure, which would clearly show the mandibular canal, the cavity that contains the nerves in the jaw. Based on canal position, researchers confirmed it was an adult jaw. The Mata Menge humans had indeed been incredibly small, just like *H. floresiensis* from Liang Bua!

Dr. Kaifu and associates next carried out the customary detailed morphological comparisons of the specimen to well-known specimens like *Australopithecus afarensis* from three million or more years ago, *H. habilis* from approximately two million years ago, *H. erectus* from approximately one million years ago (early Java Man), *H. erectus* from approximately 700,000 years ago (Peking Man), and, of course, the Liang Bua *H. floresiensis*.

The examination led Dr. Kaifu and the team to conclude the fossils from Mata Menge strongly resembled those of the Liang Bua *H. floresiensis*. They also established that the fossils showed a resemblance to early Java Man.

"First, there's the mandible, not as primitive as *Australopithecus afarensis* or *H. habilis* but with characteristics common to early Java Man and *H. floresiensis* from Liang Bua," Dr. Kaifu told me. "The teeth are also close to early Java Man's. As I said previously, the teeth of *H. floresiensis* from Liang Bua, that is, the teeth of the LB1 skeleton, and the LB6/1 mandible from a different individual found there later are a mosaic of both primitive and specialized characteristics. However, the specialization we see in the Liang Bua specimens—four cusps and the crown shape, shorter front to back than its width—is absent in the So'a Basin fossils from 700,000 years ago. If anything, the So'a Basin teeth are closer to the teeth of early Java Man."

The fact that the cusps—protrusions on the molar crowns—were simplified down to four is something that *H. floresiensis* shares with us modern humans: a curious specialization. Considering all his collected data—from Java Man fossils, Liang Bua's *H. floresiensis*, and the So'a Basin speci-

Fig. 5-10: Fossilized adult human mandible (lower jaw fragment, right side), 700,000 years old, from So'a Basin.

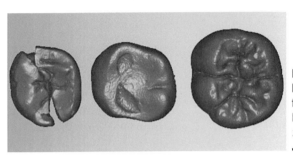

Fig. 5-11: Comparison of left mandibular molars from (left to right) So'a Basin fossil, Liang Bua *H. floresiensis*, and a modern Japanese.

mens gathered by hand and examined thoroughly, what kind of scenario could Dr. Kaifu derive?

It is simply this: early Java Man → So'a Basin humans → *H. floresiensis* from Liang Bua Cave. "It's not just the fossils," concluded Dr. Kaifu. "The stone tools are other evidence. The existence of the same types of stone tools at Mata Menge and at Liang Bua Cave implies continuity over this period. There's also no evidence of dramatic change in the fauna for hundreds of thousands of years, so the environment was probably stable as well during this time."

What Makes Us Human?

What I find astounding is that fossils from more than 700,000 years ago discovered in the So'a Basin also came from small individuals, just like the hobbit of Liang Bua Cave alive hundreds of thousands of years later. If anything, the mandible from the So'a Basin (SOA-MM1)—compared against the *H. floresiensis* holotype specimen LB1 and the LB6/1 mandible from a second individual also found in Liang Bua Cave—turned out to be slightly smaller.

The surprises just kept on coming! Clearly there's a need for greater precision and caution in the debate. "Nonetheless, we now know the extreme dwarfing experienced by early *Homo* on Flores dates back a very long time, more than 700,000 years ago," observed Dr. Kaifu. "This fact alone is quite a surprise. The strata where we find stone tools on Flores date back about a million years, which means those early Flores hominins underwent that much size reduction over just 300,000 years after reaching the island and then remained at that size."

If you protest that this seems impossible, then it's worth recalling the extreme example of red deer on the English island of Jersey who shrank to just one-sixth their original size over the course of only 6,000 years. "This degree of dwarfism has never been known to occur among primates, however," continued Dr. Kaifu, "and it's truly surprising that it could have happened among a group of humans."

The discovery of such tiny humans in Liang Bua Cave had sent shockwaves around the world. The estimate that they lived until as recently as just 12,000 years ago only poured more fuel on the fire. Current estimates push that date back to 50,000 years at the latest.

The discovery in the So'a Basin strongly suggests the *H. floresiensis* ancestors underwent rapid dwarfing as soon as they reached the island and remained that way. It's shocking to discover we humans are as powerfully impacted by an isolated island environment as other common animals are. The discovery raises new questions about the nature of being human. This is one of the reasons their paper was such big news, with over 600 different media outlets carrying the story, according to Dr. Kaifu and his team.

I should also mention another significant result of this discovery was to effectively put to rest at long last the competing hypothesis that *H. floresiensis* had been nothing more than a diseased *H. sapiens*. It turns out that we *Homo sapiens* hadn't been born yet, 700,000 years ago, not even in the cradle of modern humankind, Africa.

Envisioning the World of *Homo floresiensis*

Having reviewed and learned from the new discoveries noted above, let's once again imagine the world of *H. floresiensis*. Jump back around one million years to a time when ocean levels were much lower than today's, when everything from the Indochina Peninsula to the islands of Sumatra, Java, Bali, Borneo, and all the spaces between them formed a single vast land mass known as Sundaland. Somehow traversing Sundaland and crossing either the Lombok Strait or the Makassar Strait—the end of the landmass at that time—a small group of early *Homo* continued on, making a few more ocean crossings of several kilometers each, finally arriving on today's Flores Island.

We know nothing of how they made these crossings. It's unlikely they possessed navigational skills, meaning they were probably castaways who arrived on Flores by a cascade of accidents and chance. That's one widespread interpretation. We know *Homo erectus* appear in Asia between 1.7 and 1.2 million years ago, and early-period stone tools found on Flores date back one million years—more than ample time for accidents to happen.

Flores then was an "island-rule" island: home to pygmy Stegodon elephants only 1.5 meters tall at the shoulder and giant scavenger Marabou storks towering up to 1.8 meters; where gigantic rats and enormous Komodo monitor lizards, those dragons of our time and space, walked the land. The band of early *Homo* blended into this topsy-turvy realm where the big got small and the small grew big. They shrank to barely more than a meter tall, living in a world of dragons, gigantic rats, and towering scavenger storks—a *Lord of the Rings* universe!

I believe it was a harsh environment for these little humans, and their chances of survival were slim at best if they dropped their guard and were attacked by a Komodo dragon or a giant Marabou stork. At the same time, however, we should remember they'd undergone dwarfism because there was no selective pressure in their environment against it. So it may also be possible that life was not quite so hard. After all, this island had no large mammalian predators like the tigers or clouded leopards in other parts of Sundaland. It was a world where it was relatively safe to be tiny, and so these early *Homo* continued to live on, even after severe shrinkage. Indeed, their diminutive size came from excellent adaptation to their environment.

They made primitive stone tools and may have hunted more easily, catching prey like giant rats or possibly stalking elephant calves. Going by the record written in their stone tools, these tiny humans lived here for a very long time, just short of a million years. There may have been scattered volcanic eruptions destroying nearby life, but there was no disaster that would have impacted the whole island. They lived on through many ice ages in the company of dwarf elephants, giant rats, and dragons.

The latest evidence they left behind in their stone tools dates back 50,000 years. That roughly corresponds to the time when modern humans, we *H. sapiens,* finally arrived on the Australian continent, after leaving Africa and then reaching Sundaland and going beyond it to spread across littoral Southeast Asia. At that time did these two members of genus *Homo* ever meet? If they did, what happened between them? Were those meetings amicable or hostile? Was there cross-breeding? It seems to me that a drama unfolded on Flores that deserves special mention in the annals of human history. I can only look forward to the results of future research and new discoveries.

Flores mythology tells of tiny human-like creatures, the Ebu Gogo. In a local island language, *"ebu"* means "grandmother" and *"gogo"* is someone who eats anything. Ebu Gogo are pranksters, and the village people burned down their homes. When I think of the timing of the disappearance of *H. floresiensis,* the myth seems to recount a plausible scenario: *H. floresiensis* driven out by modern humans. It gives me the chills to feel this dovetailing of myth and history.

Dizzying Diversity

Now let's step back a moment and take a bird's eye view of the times in which *H. floresiensis* lived. For that, let's look at Flores Island as a point on a world map. You might want to return to our map in Chapter 1 (Fig.1-10) showing the distribution of human populations over time and refresh your memory, now that you're acquainted with *H. floresiensis.*

Of that world some 700,000 years ago, around the time of *H. floresiensis*-like fossils from the So'a Basin, we can say the following: *H. erectus* and more advanced forms of archaic *Homo* were already living everywhere from Africa to the furthest reaches of the low and middle latitudes of the Eurasian continent.

Second, these archaic groups of *Homo* had not yet advanced to regions cut off to them by open ocean, such as Australia or the Americas. What's more, they hadn't established themselves in extremely cold regions like the Scandinavian Peninsula or Siberia. Yet *H. erectus* had made humanity's first foray out of Africa, spread across Eurasia, crossed little stretches of open sea, and made a life for themselves on Flores Island.

Even if those first arrivals on Flores were accidental castaways, they were great adventurers and discoverers who expanded their territory over vast distances from Africa, where they had begun.

If we look only at Asia back then, in addition to the Javan *H. erectus* lineage, there was the Peking Man *H. erectus* lineage. The line resulting in *H. floresiensis* could be called a third lineage. Since there are still many parts of Asia where adequate investigations have yet to be carried out, it's likely that the presence of peoples of even greater diversity will come to light in the future.

What, then, was the world like for *H. floresiensis* only some 100,000 years ago, not long before their final days? In Africa, we *Homo sapiens* had already made our start. However, it would be some time before we left that continent and populated the far corners of the world. Our forerunners who expanded their habitable territories in Eurasia were late archaic *Homo*, most widely represented by the Neanderthals. They advanced a little farther than *H. erectus* had, making incursions into the southern parts of Siberia. In Asia, meanwhile, there was another lineage that culminated in the Denisovans, who you'll recall were the archaic *Homo* group discovered in Russia's Altai region, with fossils dating back more than 50,000 years. Also at that time there was a group in today's China broadly referred to as Chinese late archaic *Homo*.

And let's not forget that all this time there was Java Man still hanging on in Sundaland while another early *Homo* group was making a life for itself on Flores Island. It was a time when both the new and the old worlds coexisted and different human species lived contemporaneously. When I reflect on that time, my head truly swims at the thought of all that diversity. The question that informs this entire volume—Why are we *H. sapiens* the only human species left today?—first came to me as I cast my mind back from this homogenous age to that variegated world of the past.

And now, let me tell you another story, a tale I'll later tell in detail of yet another discovery made about that more-than-adequately-diverse world of ancient humans. Mini spoiler: it has Asian origins.

A fourth Asian *erectus*-grade *Homo*?

Just as the third Asian *erectus*-grade *Homo*, *H. floresiensis* challenged the conventional wisdom about human evolution, this find is forcing us to reassess our understanding of Asian premodern *Homo* as well. The groundbreaking knowledge came to us from Taiwan, a place where no fossils of ancient humans had ever been found before. And its discovery was made by a team in which Dr. Kaifu played a central role. Let's see how this new chapter unfolds with its unique narrative.

CHAPTER 6

Up from Taiwan's Ocean Floor

New Fossil from Penghu, Taiwan

The preceding chapters have detailed the research into *H. floresiensis*, aka Flores Man, up through the So'a Basin discovery of 2016. But let me backtrack a bit to tell another, earlier story.

Right after New Year's 2015, when I'd begun researching and reporting for this book, Dr. Kaifu rang me on my cellphone. Since most of our communication was by email, I found this a bit unusual. "I'm giving a press conference," he told me. "Can you make it?" He'd already published his detailed description of the LB1 skull, holotype specimen for Flores Man (2011); had contributed papers further advancing the debate over LB1 dwarfism and brain size (2013); and would've been writing a paper on Flores Man's teeth. So I was quite sure the call meant his hobbit teeth paper was to be published.

But I thought he must have made some quite remarkable discovery for him to hold a press conference. It turned out I was right that the press conference was to announce a remarkable new discovery, but I was very wrong about what this discovery was.

It turns out that Dr. Kaifu's paper on the hobbit's teeth was published in *PLOS ONE*, an online scientific journal, a few days after our phone call. The research presented in the paper was based on the extremely detailed work typical of Dr. Kaifu and was press-conference worthy in its own right. But that was not the press conference. If I were to write *a* newspaper headline for the press conference, it would read: Fourth Asian *erectus*-grade Human Discovered in Taiwan!

This was not Flores Man. Not Java Man. Not Peking Man. None of our three reigning Asian *erectus*-grade *Homo*. This was a fourth such primitive hominin. And it had been discovered near Taiwan, where no ancient human fossils had been previously found.

I was first stunned by the unexpected news and then experienced a flood of excitement. The lesson we'd all learned from the Flores Island discoveries was that there are mountains of things we don't know about the humans in Asia. Based on the case of Flores where, as Dr. Kaifu had put it at the time, "a totally unexpected human species was found in a completely unexpected place," it really shouldn't have been surprising that another human fossil showed up somewhere else in Asia. But I was delightfully surprised.

What kind of people had this Taiwanese archaic *Homo* been? What new knowledge and new puzzles would there be and where would they lead us? It was of the highest interest and quite profound.

The detailed paper was published the next day in *Nature Communications*, an online science journal affiliated with *Nature* magazine, under the dry title, "The First Archaic *Homo* from Taiwan." The discovery of a new ancient human fossil is always a major event, no matter where it occurs. It certainly was worth a press conference, and this news was announced simultaneously in Taiwan and Japan. It also made the news on CNN and in other international media.

This Taiwanese *Homo* had been named Penghu Man. The main points of the paper are as follows.

1. A fossil mandible (Penghu 1) discovered on the ocean floor off Taiwan was the first ancient human fossil found there.
2. The mandible had distinctive features quite different from Indonesia's Java Man and Flores Man or China's Peking Man and had been identified as that of another Asian archaic *Homo*.
3. It dated back between 450,000 and 190,000 years.
4. Post-*erectus* grade archaic *Homo* had appeared in northern China and other locations some 300,000 years ago. This discovery suggested that Penghu Man with more primitive characteristics still survived at that time in Southeast Asia. The find indicated the diversity of ancient humans in Asia and the complexity of their evolutionary history.

Writing this down even now fills me with excitement! At the time I was hooked on the find being the first from Taiwan and on its coming from the ocean floor.

You may be thinking that fossils are found by digging into earth and that it must be awfully rare to bring up fossils of ancient humans from the ocean floor. And you'd be right. Most clusters of fossils from Africa, Peking Man, Java Man, and Flores Man—all early humans—were excavated from the earth.

There are cases, of course, where fossils are covered by the ocean or ocean sediment after original burial, so it's likely there are fossil-bearing

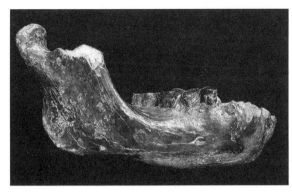

Fig. 6-1: Penghu 1
Exceptionally well-preserved Penghu 1 mandible, right half, with various primitive characteristics, with large teeth but no chin.

sediments at the bottom of the ocean. But the thought of diving down to excavate a site underwater is enough to boggle the mind. It's amazing they were able to do it this time, or so I imagined on first hearing the news.

But it turned out the Penghu Man fossil had been caught up in a bottom-trawling fishing net and reeled in with the fish catch. That's impressive enough by itself. To untrained eyes, a jawbone fossil would be a pretty dull-looking object. It was remarkable that the specimen wasn't just thrown away. Was this not a miracle: that this fossil had not been tossed aside but had been saved and eventually, by some circuitous route, spotted by a researcher? Or destiny? At the very least, it was an extraordinary stroke of good luck.

Having first been amazed simply by how the discovery came about, my mind soon turned back to this book's central theme—the story of human diversity in Asia—and I began to ponder the discovery itself and the great complexity of the evolutionary history this extraordinary story illustrated so well.

That the fossil was described as less than 190,000 years old meant it existed when Chinese late archaic *Homo*—not Peking Man—had already appeared in northern China. It was a time when Java Man was on Java, and Flores Man or their ancestors would have been around. If the fossils went back as far as 450,000 years, then even Peking Man might still have been alive. I caught glimpses of an astonishing degree of diversity and a tangled evolutionary path.

The paper announcing the find didn't come until 2015, but the story of its discovery began back in 2008. The lead author of the paper,

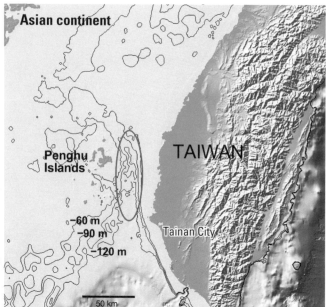

Fig. 6-2: Where the Penghu Man fossil was discovered. The Penghu Channel, where animal fossils are found in great abundance, is indicated by the oval.

Dr. Chun-Hsiang Chang, researcher in the Department of Geology at Taiwan's National Museum of Natural Science, recognized the importance of numerous animal fossils dredged up from the ocean floor in the nets of bottom-trawling fishing vessels operating in waters southwest of Taiwan. In 2008, however, Dr. Chang discovered one particularly interesting fossil mixed in among the rest. It appeared to be from a primate, but what species? The instant he asked himself that question, the path opened to the discovery of the Penghu Man.

The research surrounding this rare fossil from the bottom of the ocean was a scientific mystery story, one where study methods were figured out through trial and error. Dr. Kaifu, involved in this research from the earliest stages, tells us about it.

That's Not a Monkey—It's a Human!

To begin with a primary question, how did this discovery come about?

"Fishermen in the southern Taiwanese city of Tainan head out to sea where they practice bottom trawling, dragging weighted nets across the

Fig. 6-3: Dr. Chang with some fish and Penghu fauna fossils dredged up by a fishing boat.

ocean floor," Dr. Kaifu began. "They fish the Penghu Channel, between the main island of Taiwan and the Penghu Islands, where the ocean depth is about seventy meters. And they bring up lots and lots of fossils caught in their nets. The fossils are a bother for the fishermen, but the best specimens find their way into the hands of local dealers in antiques and curios. As there are no relevant administrative regulations, many fossils find their way into the hands of collectors. Dr. Chang heard that a local Tainan collector had a particularly interesting specimen."

Fossils dredged up in the waters near the Penghu Islands include elephant, water buffalo, horse, Père David's deer, deer, boar, raccoon dog, bear, tiger, hyena, crocodile, and turtle. All are known collectively as Penghu fauna. Many large fauna fossils are hauled up from the ocean floor because they are the right size to get snagged by the trawl nets. Dr. Kaifu showed me a photograph taken soon after a net had been hauled up and emptied on the deck, showing the condition in which the fossils had been found—what you might call a picture of fossils *in situ,* only this time not in rock.

Since the fishing boat was dragging a fishing net, it's only natural that many fish spilled onto the deck. Among the fish were blackish lumps that at first glance seemed like bits of old tree branches. What Dr. Chang is holding up in Fig. 6-3 is not an old tree branch but a water buffalo skull fossil. The surface is dark in color, but there are also bottom-dwelling

Fig. 6-4: Vast numbers of Penghu fauna fossils at Taiwan's
National Museum of Natural
Science "caught" from the
ocean floor.

sea creatures attached to it who appear here and there as white blotches. This tells us there were many sediment layers on the ocean floor in which they'd been buried. Fossils breaking off from that sediment have lain exposed on the floor of the ocean long enough for them to become home to benthos, a community of organisms living on the ocean floor. Had they been left undisturbed, it's likely the fossils would have disintegrated over time. Instead, the fossils are recovered in fishing nets. Profuse quanti- ties of Penghu fauna fossils have been "caught," to date. While some are preserved at the National Museum, a significant number are in the hands of collectors. The jaw in question was in the possession of one such collector.

"It was in 2008 that Dr. Chang noticed the mandible," continued Dr. Kaifu. "Dr. Chang's own field of research is elephants, but when he asked the local collector to show him his collection of fossils, there was one that made Dr. Chang really take notice, and he photographed it. The next year, in 2009, at an academic conference on mammals held in Taiwan, Dr. Chang showed the photograph to Dr. Masanaru Takai from the Pri- mate Research Institute at Kyoto University. Dr. Takai took one look at the picture and said, "This isn't from a monkey; it's human," and reached out to Dr. Kono and me, whom he knew to be experts on the subject. It was decided that we would start up a joint research project, and in 2010 we went to Tainan. We met the owner of the fossil, asked him to show it to us, and felt right away that this was an early human with heretofore unknown characteristics."

That was when this human from hundreds of thousands of years ago—later called Penghu Man—first became the subject of research into human evolution.

Extremely Distinctive Jaw and Teeth

"Here, this is a replica. Hold it," said Dr. Kaifu, handing it to me. It wasn't a fossil skull, just a mandible, and only the right side at that.

Back when I started reporting, I felt so tense that my hands shook whenever holding even a fossil replica. By the time I held the mandible, however, I was used to such things. Moreover, since I'd been taught the characteristics of early humans over and over, I came to understand them, even as an amateur.

Staring intently at the mandible, I picked out at least two things that marked it as neither primate nor modern human. If it were a primate, the curve depicted by the lower jaw should be in the shape of a U, while in human lower jaws the opening atop a U should be drawn as widening, becoming more like a V, or describing a parabola. Since the specimen was more like the latter, it was not a primate but closer to a human.

On the other hand, as the front of the jaw was less pointed and had no chin, it was clearly not a modern human. That was my rough impression,

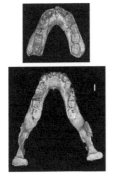 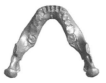

Fig. 6-5: The Penghu 1 mandible widens toward the back.
Left: Early *Homo* mandibles from Africa and Georgia (2 million–1.75 million years ago)
Middle: Penghu Man (reconstructed by 3D image processing)
Right: Chinese *H. erectus* (approx. 600,000 years ago)

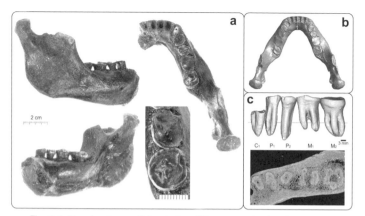

Fig. 6-6: Penghu 1 mandible photos, CT scan, and other imagery.
a: Penghu 1 mandible fossil
b: Computer virtual reconstruction based on CT data
c: (Top) Surface rendering of the teeth based on CT data
   (Bottom) Horizontal micro-CT section of the roots

and apparently I was mostly correct. Dr. Kaifu next showed me a mandible lineup, one from *H. habilis* (early African *Homo* around two million years ago) and one from Peking Man, who lived 600,000 years ago. As I've said before, having Dr. Kaifu's lab nearby was extremely convenient at times like these—he can just pull out a specimen, replica of course, as needed.

"If I were to generalize about the shape of this fossil," Dr. Kaifu started, "in ancient hominins the jaw tends to be narrow. It's often said that primate jaws are U-shaped, but even when comparing the earliest *Homo* like *H. habilis* from two million years ago and Peking Man from 600,000 years ago, the newer jaws are wider. Penghu Man clearly falls into the latter group. Another feature to note is the robustness of the jaw. Six or seven Peking Man mandibles have been discovered, but even compared to the most rugged Peking Man mandibles, Penghu Man's is more robust, even more so than Java Man's. And though Penghu 1 is the only mandible found, it's clear that Penghu Man's was very different indeed."

Dr. Kaifu restated with far greater descriptive power and confidence the impression I got from my own rough examination. He also included a brief view on the fossil's most distinctive aspect, the atypical robustness of its mandible. His words were not merely his impression but were supported by solid data. In addition to traditional measurements, Dr. Kaifu also made full use of micro-CT scanning. This allowed him to acquire 3D data and understand the fossil's internal structure.

"In the end, we brought the fossil to Japan and had CT scans taken at the University of Tokyo University Museum. Since we only have the right-half of the jaw, we asked Dr. Kono to create a mirror image of the 3D CT scan data and recreate an image of the entire jaw in order to measure its width. She also separated out CT images of teeth roots that cannot normally be seen from the surface. It turns out these are pretty strange roots. But what surprised us even more was that every tooth is extremely large. The actual incisor was missing, but even by just looking at its socket you can tell that it was also quite big."

By extracting ever more new features not visible from the fossil surface and, as always, making detailed comparisons of these features against other humans (*H. habilis* from Africa, the Dmanisi *Homo* from Georgia, Java Man, Peking Man, and others, including Neanderthals and modern humans), the research clearly established that a hitherto unnoticed group of archaic *Homo* had existed in Asia.

Aside from the fact that this species had gone unnoticed for so long, let me emphasize one particular point: even among ancient humans, the new find was distinctive for the large tooth and jaw robustness.

We'll return to this point later in this chapter. For now, however, let's consider the meaning of the phrase, "Fourth Asian *erectus*-grade *Homo*." Even conceding there's insufficient evidence—only a single jaw specimen—to declare it to be a new species, there can be no doubt another group of archaic *Homo* in Asia had followed a different evolutionary path than its contemporaries.

What Human Era Were They From?

The next thing the researchers wanted to know was how far back the fossil dated. That was difficult to determine. If the fossil were dug up on land, then there'd have been various ways of determining its age if the team could identify the strata in which it was found. But the question was how to date a specimen dredged up from the ocean floor.

In Dr. Kaifu's experience, the problem was somewhat similar to the case of the Java Man fossils discovered on the riverbed at Sambungmacan, where the team could assume the fossils had fallen into the river from strata exposed aboveground. Even in those instances, however, they still struggled to determine their age because there was no direct information about which strata they'd come from. It must be even more difficult when you find your fossils on the ocean floor.

"Normally, the fossil is assumed to be the same age as the strata where it was found," explained Dr. Kaifu, "but in this case we had no idea at all, no way of knowing what strata were on the ocean floor. There was even less information than we'd had at Sambungmacan.

"Faced with this problem, we explored several possibilities. One was past changes in sea level. If it was not one of the periods when sea levels had fallen, then no land-based fauna could have gotten there. So, based on the ocean depth where the fossil had been found, we investigated those periods over several hundreds of thousands of years when the sea level had been at least sixty meters lower than it is today and arrived at several candidate periods. We cannot arbitrarily decide, however, which period the fossil was from. So, in the end, we had to study the fossil itself."

Let's be clear on one thing: just because a hominin fossil is brought up from the seabed doesn't mean it lived in the ocean. And as Dr. Kaifu said, the land animal fossils brought up from the ocean floor today were buried in sediment when today's Penghu Channel had been dry land. Though obvious once you realize it, it bears repeating that human and other land animal fossils can be, and are, found at the bottom of the ocean.

Over the course of the past two million years of human evolution in Asia, there were repeated Ice Ages when ocean levels fell dramatically. Penghu fauna are believed to be the remains of creatures living when the ocean was more than 60 meters lower than it is today.

Taiwan and the continent are today separated by ocean, but it's known they were connected by exposed land when ocean levels fell severely in the Ice Ages. There were periods when Penghu Man could simply have walked from the continent to Taiwan, unlike Flores Man who had to make ocean crossings.

That said, the question of how to date the fossils remained. "We came up with two approaches," Dr. Kaifu explained. "One was uranium-series dating, and for this we called out to an Australian researcher with a solid track record. The other is a method where you compare the fluorine and sodium ratios in the bone. For this we consulted Dr. Matsuura at Ocha-nomizu University. The approach involves slicing the bone itself. The only cutter we had available in Taiwan was a huge, intimidating device used for slicing minerals. That struck us as a bit too big for the job, so we had the fossil brought to Japan, borrowed a thin diamond cutter from a researcher in our museum's Department of Science and Engineering, and very carefully cut the bone. We sent one small fragment to Australia for uranium-series dating while we analyzed the slice here using our museum's electron probe microanalyzer to determine the amounts of fluorine and sodium present."

First, uranium-series dating. This method uses the fact that uranium, a radioactive material, decays into various nuclides with different half-lives until it finally becomes a stable lead isotope. By carefully selecting and comparing the ratios of the uranium isotopes and the nuclides that they pass through along the way, you can determine how much time has elapsed since the specimen stopped exchanging matter with the outside (i.e., in the case of living organisms, when it died). The precondition for using this method with fossils is that the fossil must have been preserved in a closed system—that is, in a system in which it did not exchange matter with the outside—while buried in sediment.

The strength of uranium-series dating is its very precise dating. This is because the method uses the half-life of radioactive materials, an exactly determined physical process, almost as if using a clock. If this approach proved successful, then Dr. Kaifu's team would be able to instantly determine the age of Penghu Man.

"However," said Dr. Kaifu, "when the figure came back from Australia, it was only ten thousand years."

Ten thousand years? If that were true, it would be as big a shock as when initial measurements had put the age of *H. floresiensis* at only 12,000 years. Ten thousand years ago *H. sapiens,* we modern humans, had already populated Taiwan. It would mean we modern humans had coexisted with Penghu Man. Could that possibly be true?

"The date was too recent," stated Dr. Kaifu. "Before we even started worrying about whether *H. sapiens* could have already arrived, the fact is the region where the Penghu fauna lived would have been underwater at that time.

"I consulted Dr. Matsuura and we concluded that it was possible—since uranium is also present in seawater—that the uranium in the fossil had been contaminated by uranium in the ocean water. If that was the case, it would mean the precondition for a successful uranium-series dating—that the subject had been preserved in a closed system—had not been met. The uranium in the specimen had been almost completely replaced the last time the strata containing the fossil was submerged, and we had instead been measuring the age of the seawater uranium.

"On the other hand," continued Dr. Kaifu, "by carrying out these tests, we were able to confirm that all the fossils we were looking at came out the same on the uranium-series dating, which meant they had been deposited on the ocean floor at approximately the same time. So in that sense, it was very worth having done."

Now everything hung on measuring the specimen's fluorine and sodium. "The way this works," Dr. Kaifu explained, "is that fluorine is an element not originally found in bones, so any fluorine we found would have been absorbed from the outside. In other words, it would have to have penetrated the fossil after it was buried in sediment. "Conversely, sodium exists in bones originally and leaches out. Since the external environment for fossils that had the same deposition history as Penghu 1—deposited and buried during the same period and in the same place—would have come from a similar environment and should show similar fluorine and sodium values, we were able to do relative dating to determine which fossils are older and which are newer."

Yet even after you determine the fossils' relative ages, you still need another indicator benchmark to find absolute ages. In this case, Dr. Kaifu and colleagues decided to measure not only the fluorine and sodium content of their Penghu 1 specimen but also the fluorine and sodium content in a vast number of Penghu fauna fossils as they searched for a clue to Penghu Man's age.

Hyenas Hold the Key

To summarize: Fluorine does not originally exist in bones, but bones absorb fluorine while buried in sediment; sodium is originally in bones but leaches out while bones are buried. Therefore, if Dr. Kaifu and colleagues could use the ratios of fluorine and sodium in the Penghu fauna to determine which fossils were older and newer (or which from lower or higher strata), they could then determine Penghu 1's relative position in the strata.

The best-known Penghu Fauna are elephants, water buffalos, horses, Père David's deer (also known as the milu or elaphure), boars, raccoon dogs, bears, tigers, hyenas, crocodiles, turtles, and more. Since we only know about the fossils snagged and dredged up in trawl nets, they tend to be from large fauna. If there were any that lived for a limited period, and

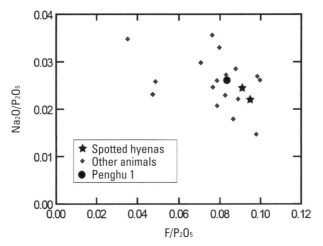

Fig. 6-7: Comparison of relative fluorine (F) and sodium (Na) contents in fossil animal bones from the Penghu Channel.

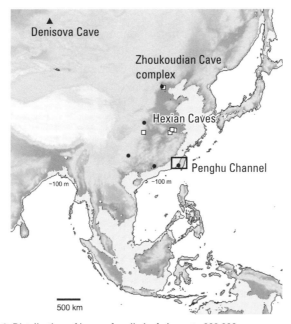

Fig. 6-8: Distribution of hyena fossils in Asia up to 200,000 years ago.
The primitive giant hyena (*Pachycrocuta*) (□) was replaced by the invading spotted hyena (●).

became extinct at a certain time, or suddenly emerged at a particular time, they could serve as index fossils used as absolute indicators for dating and allow the scientists to narrow down the possible age of Penghu 1.

"What we first had to confirm was whether an elephant, water buffalo, or anything else that came up was the same age as Penghu 1. That's because there was always the possibility that it was accidentally mixed in among the others. So, we plotted the fluorine content and sodium content of about twenty different specimens and found Penghu 1 came in smack in the middle. From this we knew Penghu 1 came from the same era as these other animals.

"Once we knew that, we then zeroed in on the spotted hyena. Dr. Takai from the Primate Research Institute drew on his extensive experience with a broad range of animal fossils and primates to pull the information together for us."

In the figure plotted by Dr. Kaifu and colleagues (Fig. 6-7), Penghu 1 and the spotted hyena are in relatively close proximity. Overall, however, Penghu 1 appears to be slightly more recent than the spotted hyena, coming out as being from the same period or one slightly more recent than the spotted hyena, even after factoring in the margin of measurement error.

When were spotted hyenas present in the same place as Penghu 1? If that could be determined, it would be a valuable clue for determining the age of the Penghu 1 fossil. Dr. Kaifu next pointed to a map showing the distribution of hyena fossils in Asia. "At this time, hyenas were widespread in Asia," he explained. "We found their fossils, and at a point in time the species changed. The white squares on the map indicate a more primitive, large-bodied species called the giant hyena. The round symbols indicate the spotted hyena, which came in and replaced them.

"It's possible this transition happened around Zhoukoudian, famous as the locality where Peking Man was discovered, around 450,000 years ago. However, in the south of China, closer to Taiwan, giant hyenas still lived on as late as 200,000 years ago, and spotted hyenas are only found in sites more recent than 200,000 years ago. In that case, we can assume the spotted hyenas found among the Penghu fauna are also more recent than 200,000 years ago. Since our conclusion was that Penghu 1 was either more recent or from the same age as the spotted hyenas, that would make it younger than 200,000 years old."

This new estimate was quite a step forward. It seemed that the idea of using the spotted hyena as a benchmark species had been a breakthrough.

Yet even so, it was still a vague figure. If you say younger than 200,000 years old, that could mean 50,000 years ago, or 10,000 years ago.

"So now," continued Dr. Kaifu, "we return to the beginning. We do know the fluctuations in ocean depth over the last several hundred thousand years. The periods when ocean levels would have been lower more recently than 200,000 years ago would have been between 70,000 and 10,000 years ago, and before that, between 190,000 and 130,000 years ago, and that's about it. So our conclusion is that it has to be during one of these two periods. However, if I'm going to be a stickler for details, I also have to mention it's possible the spotted hyena arrived in northern China a little farther back. Add that to our considerations, and we'd also have to note the possibility that Penghu 1 goes back as far as 450,000 years."

It was 200,000 years ago that the spotted hyena moved into southern China and replaced the giant hyena. The time after that when ocean levels fell was from 190,000 years ago onward. If that's true, then the best estimate at present seems to be that Penghu 1 is also from a time more recent than 190,000 years ago.

What does all this time calculation mean? "If Penghu Man existed 190,000 years ago, as our results suggest, then Peking Man had already disappeared," continued Dr. Kaifu. "In China there was a group of hominins we refer to as the Chinese late archaic *Homo*. If we think in terms of the Eurasian continent, there were also Neanderthals. And another group of archaic *Homo* called the Denisovans also showed up. This would mean that primitive-looking *Homo* still survived here in the midst of all these other humans."

Come to think of it, also at this time, further south, Java Man was still living on Java, as was *H. floresiensis* on Flores Island. That farthest north of all the Asian *H. erectus*, Peking Man, may have vanished, but various groups of late archaic *Homo* were appearing in the north. Had the territorial map of Asian continent become one with late archaic *Homo* in the north and *Homo erectus* in the south?

Whatever the case, that is the extent of what we can extrapolate at this point about the era of Penghu 1. If in the future another specimen is found, or we find a new method to investigate these issues, we may be able to pinpoint the era more precisely. For now, however, this is the best we can do.

The next question we naturally must ask is what kind of human this Penghu Man was. Even a first glance showed Penghu 1 had distinctive features. Since we have gone so far as to call Penghu Man the fourth *erectus*-grade Asian *Homo,* the thought also runs through our minds they might possibly be an entirely new species altogether.

"It is hard to judge whether they're a new species or not, with only a single jawbone to work with," observed Dr. Kaifu. "As of now, we have not even assigned it a scientific name. Ideally, I want there to be a skull found in Taiwan. A skull would decide it. At the same time, the question if it truly represents a new species leads us to another issue—the real diversity of archaic hominins in Asia."

What was the relationship between Penghu Man and the other Asian archaic humans—Java Man, Peking Man, and Flores Man? Before we can meaningfully discuss the question, we need to observe the bone minutely again.

The World's Thickest Jaw

Penghu Man displays characteristics different than those of Java Man, Peking Man, the hobbit, and Flores Man. The jaw is quite wide, a comparatively advanced characteristic, but thick and massive. And the teeth are massive. Robust teeth and jaws are characteristics of very ancient humans.

Does this mean they were completely isolated and unlike other humans? Not necessarily. One of the first things you must do when discovering a new human fossil is to search to see whether other similar fossils have been found already. When Dr. Kaifu saw Penghu 1, he immediately recalled a Chinese fossil that had not yet received much research.

"There was a human skull fossil discovered in China in the 1980s in a place called Hexian in Anhui province," Dr. Kaifu told me. "I'd been interested in it and thought it was another pretty strange fossil. However, the dominant hypotheses in China going back many years had been that the modern Chinese evolved from Peking Man, and so, even though the shape of the Hexian skull was clearly very different, it had also been declared a relative of Peking Man. A quite thick jawbone had also been discovered in Hexian, a fact that also stuck in memory. So, I went back and checked the literature, and when I saw the photographs from Hexian, I thought these really resemble the Penghu 1 mandible. I felt there might well be a connection between them."

The Hexian fossil dates back some 400,000 years, a time corresponding to the closing days of Peking Man. For the time being, let's tentatively dub it "Hexian Man." In his paper on Penghu 1, Dr. Kaifu compared Penghu 1 to various ancient humans, including Hexian Man. And his results led to a brilliant conclusion in line with his own diagnosis.

In this case, all we have to compare is a jaw and some teeth. First to consider is that jaw. "We've plotted the width of the front part of the Penghu 1 mandible (the corpora) on the horizontal x axis and the height of the mandible on the vertical y axis," explained Dr. Kaifu. "The figures are measurements at the first molar. The 'P' on the chart is for Penghu, and you will see that while it's not very high, it is extremely thick across. Even compared to Peking Man, it is markedly thick. In the sense of height versus thickness, it's quite extreme—much thicker than the African *H. erectus* of some two million to 1.5 million years ago, *H. habilis,* and *H. ergaster.* It would be safe to say it's the thickest jaw in the world."

Bear in mind here that it's the thickness of Penghu 1's jaw proportionate to its height that is the "thickest in the world." If we're talking only about the mandible's thickness, then there are more robust *H. habilis* specimens on hand. There are also more robust specimens from the group that includes early Java Man, with *Meganthropus* and its enormous jawbone. However, if we look at the proportion of different jaw heights and thicknesses, Penghu 1 had the thickest jaw of all early *Homo*, late archaic *Homo*, and modern humans found to date.

"Next, we plotted the values for the Hexian specimen. On the chart this is indicated by 'H.' These are values taken from the literature. When we do this, we see that—while it may not be as extreme as Penghu Man—the jaw is still quite thick. When we next compare their teeth, the Hexian "H" and the Penghu 1 "P" wind up largely overlapping. This size is on par with *H. habilis.*"

The horizontal axis on this chart shows the buccolingual diameter (BL) for the second molar. The vertical axis is the mesiodistal diameter (MD). These are, respectively, the "width" of the teeth when looking at them from above as set in the jaw, and the "length" of the teeth when viewed in the "closer to farther" direction (front to back). In other words, they're the width and the length of the teeth.

Viewed in terms of this particular relationship, the charted positions for Penghu Man and Hexian Man matched almost completely. "They are clearly larger than the teeth of the Chinese *H. erectus* Peking Man," Dr. Kaifu explained, "and fall into a range overlapping early Java Man fossils with robust jaws and teeth and early African *Homo*." In terms of these characteristics, it seems Penghu Man and Hexian Man were very much alike.

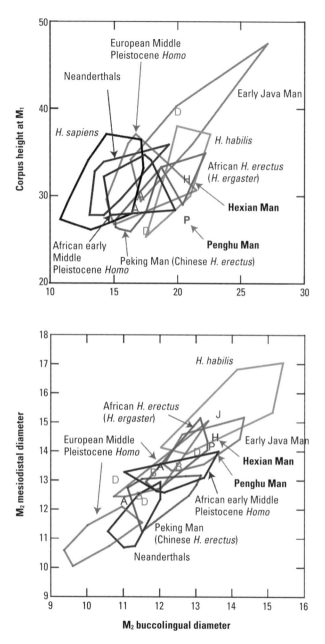

Fig. 6-9: Comparisons of mandibular corpora and mandibular second molars of Penghu Man, Hexian Man, and other ancient humans.

It's also significant that the places where the two specimens were excavated are relatively close—only 900 kilometers on the map. Today, there is ocean between where the 400,000-year-old Hexian Man and the 190,000-year-old-or-more-recent Penghu Man were found (with Penghu 1 found at the bottom of the ocean). But do remember there were at least five times in the last 400,000 years when ocean levels dropped and it would have been possible to walk back and forth across that distance.

Is it possible that Penghu Man and Hexian Man were in the same group of archaic *Homo*? Could they possibly have flourished from the south of China to today's Taiwan during that long period? If so, we need to rewrite the history of human evolution as we have understood it so far.

Until now, it had been assumed that masticatory apparatus—jaws, teeth, and other features—size reduction was the evolutionary path followed by humankind ever since the emergence of the genus *Homo*. Brain size increase and masticatory apparatus shrinkage were seen as a consistent trend that was part of the very definition of genus *Homo*.

However, the group encompassing Penghu Man and Hexian Man might be humans who went in a different direction, a direction in which they maintained their thick jaws and massive teeth—not merely maintained them but evolved to have extremely distinctive teeth and the heaviest jaws of all.

Be it Flores Man, whose brains shrank despite their being human, or Penghu Man, there have been more and more discoveries in Asia that are overturning our conventional wisdom. The impact of the discovery of Penghu Man will not stop here and may highlight the problem of connecting Java Man and Peking Man, an issue that's been stuck for many years. Why? Because Penghu Man and Hexian Man are humans who drive a figurative wedge between Java Man and Peking Man, which heretofore had been thought to be regional groups of *H. erectus*.

Human Evolution in Asia Still Full of Mystery

If Penghu Man ultimately proves to have lived more recently than 190,000 years ago, as Dr. Kaifu and colleagues predict, then it's possible a group of *Homo* retaining primitive characteristics continued to survive with Chinese late archaic *Homo*. If that is the case, how did late archaic *Homo* and *Homo erectus* divide their territories? Many mysteries remain. We still don't fully understand the different categories and evolutionary backgrounds of the Chinese late archaic *Homo*. Future developments in this field could prove thrilling.

Again, I'd like to note that around this very same time, various groups of late archaic *Homo*, like the Denisovans and the Neanderthals, were pressing in on northwestern Asia, while far to the south Java Man was living in today's Java, then part of prehistoric Sundaland. And let's not forget even further away from Taiwan lived Flores Man on their island.

It's also deeply interesting to examine Figs. 6-10 and 6-11, two maps depicting the distribution of the Asian archaic *Homo*. Peking Man would've already disappeared about 400,000 years ago, but let's add them to our map for perspective.

Until recently, Java Man and Peking Man were considered to be simply regional groups of the same species, *H. erectus*, and had not come in for much more serious research than that. Now, however, we're aware of Penghu Man and Hexian Man from south China as similar to each other. Both groups lived farther south than Peking Man's territory and were that much closer to where Java Man lived in Sundaland.

If we consider Java Man and Peking Man to simply be southern and northern groups of *H. erectus,* then from their physical location alone we might anticipate that both Penghu Man and Hexian Man will prove to display intermediary characteristics that bridge the differences between them, giving us Peking Man in the north, Java Man in the south, and some still undiscovered group or groups living between these two populations and likely displaying intermediary characteristics. What we have here is an image of many different groupings of Asian *H. erectus* linked together, their particular characteristics generally mapping along a broad north-south gradient.

It seems every time we acquire a new piece of knowledge about human evolution in Asia with all its still-unknown aspects, that find just adds new mysteries to the mix. Indeed, both Penghu Man and Hexian Man were discovered in that region between Java Man and Peking Man but have proved to bear unique primitive features unlike those of Peking Man or Java Man.

"Apart from the debate over whether Penghu Man or Hexian Man groups represented new species or not, the discovery did knock down our previous prediction that there would have been *H. erectus* groups connected through slight variations by region throughout Asia," said Dr. Kaifu. "Until now we've lumped Peking Man and Java Man together as *H. erectus*. But now

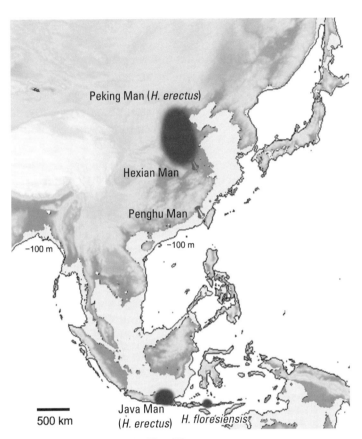

Fig. 6-10: The Asia of Penghu Man (A).
If Penghu Man lived around 400,000 years ago, they would have occupied a middle territory between Peking Man in the north and Java Man and Flores Man in the south. The "-100m" map notation indicates the approximate coastline when ocean levels fell during Ice Ages. Note the land bridge linking Taiwan to the mainland.

we're confronted with new questions like what is this species we call *H. erectus*, when and where did they evolve, and how did the complicated structure of different Asian groups that we now know of come about."

Quite unexpectedly, the scientists had been provided a new opportunity requiring them to update the conventional wisdom. Of course, exploring this new territory requires not only a thoroughgoing comparison of the Java Man and Peking Man fossils already on hand but also new fossil evidence. But that's an issue for the future.

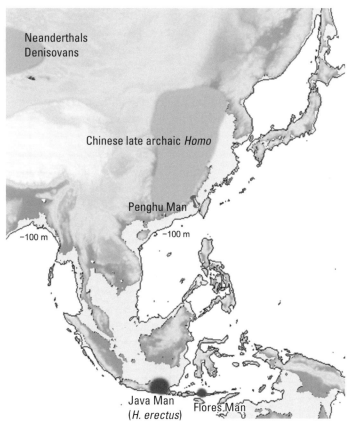

Fig. 6-11: The Asia of Penghu Man (B).
If Penghu Man lived around 100,000 years ago, Chinese late archaic *Homo*, Neanderthals, and Denisovans appear on the map. As of this writing, it's undetermined whether Penghu Man lived during period (A) or period (B). However, these two maps make the complicated mosaic of humankind past in Asia clear.

"The only thing I can say for sure at this point is that what we'd all learned in the past—that there were only Peking Man and Java Man in Asia—was not correct," reflects Dr. Kaifu. "Something far more diverse, far more complex, took place here. Taiwan is a place where no ancient human fossils had been found until now. We were all looking at previously discovered fossils from places like Java and China and generalizing about all of Asia based on them alone. But now that a completely unpredicted example has been found in a place different from what we had expected, we no longer know what other discoveries may be made in other unexpected places. That's how I see it today."

Still Much to Learn

What kind of discoveries will be made in Asia in the future? For one, I hear there have been new developments in Java Man research regarding stone tools that hadn't been studied closely.

Stone tools have also been discovered in association with Flores Man, suggesting that we've finally entered a new stage when the Asian early *Homo* can also be studied through an approach based on the culture of stone tools. There's still a tendency in Japan and elsewhere for archaeology and anthropology to be perceived as two distinct fields, but in the future they should be seen as two complementary fields of research on human evolution. It's my personal hope that when those two fields finally move in sync, we'll be that much closer to achieving a level of resolution in our understanding of the lives of our archaic predecessors in Asia and I might be able to write my novel describing the way they lived.

Looking at Flores Man, we can see the way to new discoveries at Liang Bua and So'a Basin. Strata on Sulawesi Island and elsewhere, however, have yielded ancient stone tools, and fossils of humans that crossed the ocean to those islands may be found in the future. It will be extremely interesting to perhaps find out whether those humans were also hobbits or were big people.

Regarding Penghu Man and Hexian Man, we're likely to learn much more about their origins when we have more specimens. If we do have more, then the day may yet come when they'll be recognized as new species. It was truly remarkable for Penghu 1 to have been found on the ocean bed, which gave us the sort of new knowledge that declares, "This, too, can happen." The next time something of great interest gets dredged up in a net, there's a much better chance that rich catch will land in the hands of expert professionals.

The rush of amazing new discoveries in Asia from the start of this twenty-first century suggests the strong possibility that more unexpected humans will be discovered in more unexpected places in the years to come.

CHAPTER 7

Lost in Evolution

Why Asia?

In the search for what got lost in the evolution of humankind, many researchers are looking to Asia. Why, and why now?

"As you might imagine, research into human evolution has thus far focused largely on Africa and Europe," explains Dr. Kaifu. "There are 'black box' issues all across Asia even now, and I want to shed more light on these. As an Asian myself, I think it is a little sad that we know about Cro-Magnon and Neanderthal humans in Europe while not knowing who was in Asia."

Even as he maintains his professional calm, Dr. Kaifu nonetheless burns with a quiet intensity. Thanks to his efforts to squarely address the history of human evolution in Asia, we now know that a dazzling diversity of humans, sometimes quite unexpected, lived in this region in ways that suited their times spanning only a few tens of thousands of years, a few hundreds of thousands of years ago.

So let's now consider in conclusion the difficult question that is the theme of this book: why is there no one but us *Homo sapiens* left today? What is the current state of anthropological and archaeological knowledge? To what degree have researchers agreed on the evidence, and what conclusions can be derived? And building on those conclusions, what sort of research will be carried on in the future?

Pulling Everything Together: Asia's Diverse Humans

Let me begin with a brief recapitulation of what we know. It is possible that Java Man, barely known yet famous enough to appear in Japanese history textbooks, was already living on Java 1.2 million years ago and survived until some 50,000 years ago, evolving considerably during this period. Continuous change can be seen from early Java Man (1.2 million to 800,000 years ago) at Sangiran and Trinil through to Sambungmacan (circa 300,000 years ago) to late Java Man (circa 100,000 years ago) at Ngandong.

H. floresiensis, aka Flores Man, who was discovered in the early twenty-first century and was a massive sensation, seems to have lived on Flores Island until up to about 50,000 years ago. Their ancestors reached

the island by about one million years ago. There also may have been similar types of humans on another Indonesian island, Sulawesi, and on Luzon
in the Philippines.

While Peking Man disappeared long before Java Man and *H. floresiensis*, a different form of archaic *Homo* with an extremely robust jaw lived
in southern China and Taiwan about 400,000 to 100,000 years ago.

This last discovery might now make it necessary to reevaluate the conventional wisdom that Peking Man and Java Man were both *H. erectus*.
If it's correct to state that *H. erectus* diffused widely throughout Asia and
that Peking Man and Java Man represent regional groups of the species,
then there should be intermediate *H. erectus* variants between them who
exhibit gradual feature changes. Now, however, we have an entirely unan-
ticipated thick-jawed archaic *Homo* group.

There are also faint signs here and there of late archaic *Homo* more
advanced than *H. erectus*. The Chinese late archaic *Homo* is a human
who emerged after Peking Man in China and, while their age isn't precisely known, are believed to date between 360,000 and 100,000 years
ago. Likewise, we now know that Neanderthals existed at the same time
in the same place as the enigmatic Denisovans living 100,000 to 50,000
years ago in Denisova Cave in Russia's Altai Mountains. Remains of both
humans have been found in that cave.

Although there is perennial controversy over the dating, it's clear that
a great many species of humans (i.e., genus *Homo*) were living in Asia
going back hundreds of thousands of years, or even as recently as only
tens of thousands of years.

Yet now, humankind is homogenous. There is only *H. sapiens*. How
are we to understand this? What could have happened between that era of
diverse human species and our homogenous present?

No Evidence of Contact

"In that regard, we're all doing our research in the hope of finding evidence," says Dr. Kaifu. "The thing I most want to find is the moment of
contact between *H. sapiens* and late archaic *Homo*. We haven't found it
yet. Even in Europe, where research is quite advanced, there is a geological
layer that is without remains from the end of the Neanderthals through the
start of the era of *H. sapiens,* and we haven't found any concrete evidence
of direct contact. At present, we simply don't know what happened."

One possible model is "replacement" of Neanderthal (late archaic *Homo*) by Cro-Magnon (modern humans). There is a tremendous amount of debate on this subject. Just going by what I've come across, a whole range of hypotheses have been put forth: from the Conflict Hypothesis, in which Neanderthals were defeated in battle, to theories involving climate change, volcanic eruptions, disease, interbreeding, and differences in learning ability. Academic circles aside, when the mainstream media report on the subject, explanations of various quality get thrown together, often sowing more confusion. Let's see what can be said based solely on scientific fact.

"With regard to Europe, it seems certain there was a period of overlap between Neanderthal and Cro-Magnon," says Dr. Kaifu. "It used to be said that this period lasted about 10,000 years. Now, however, this estimate has been refined, and the leading theory is that the overlap lasted about 5,000 years. I reiterate that there's still no archaeological evidence they encountered one another. Still, based on recent dramatic advances in DNA analysis, it's been claimed there was some limited interbreeding between them."

Putting together the overlap period and the genetic mixing that genetic anthropology has found, it seems beyond reasonable doubt that there was some contact between the two. Could it be that the contact just wasn't clear enough to be seen archaeologically? Whatever the case may be, a great many words have been expended over many years by experts and amateurs alike on the notion of Neanderthal replacement by Cro-Magnon in Europe. It would require another book—and a very thick book at that—to discuss it adequately, so let's leave it at that for now.

We Know Even Less about Asia

"We're even further behind in understanding Asia," said Dr. Kaifu. "We still don't know when *H. erectus* disappeared in Asia, and the debate over when *H. sapiens* arrived is also very much in flux." As to the question of how long Flores Man or Java Man lived on, there is a strong possibility that our current dating will change in the future with further research and technology advances. The timeline for the arrival of *H. sapiens* in Asia is likewise uncertain, with no consensus as yet.

Among the reasons for the lack of agreement is that fewer scientists conduct research into human evolution and diffusion in Asia than in

Europe. There are also fewer strata of limestone, in which fossils are more easily preserved, from those eras where we might anticipate that human fossils could be found. However, it also may simply be that neither the strata nor the fossils have been discovered yet. So European research still eclipses Asian when it comes to archaeological site scale as well as the quality and quantity of fossils and artifacts found.

"As to when *H. sapiens* arrived, there were researchers in the 1990s who said it happened 100,000 years ago," said Dr. Kaifu. "The idea was that *H. sapiens* remains dating to 100,000 years ago had been found in Australia, and that the species had to have passed through Asia prior to Australia. Doubts were later raised about this, leading to a new hypothesis of 80,000 years ago, which in turn has fallen out of favor as well. A paper has just been published in *Nature* stating that the oldest remains in Australia date to 65,000 years ago. Given the evidence we currently have, I believe a date of 50,000 years ago is solid."

Genetic testing technology has also become more sophisticated. In light of recent findings by nuclear genome analysis, opinions are split over the question of the arrival of *H. sapiens* in Asia, now put between 80,000 years ago (propounded chiefly by the University of Copenhagen) and 50,000 years ago (primarily championed by the Max Planck Institutes). The latter included the effect of *H. sapiens* interbreeding with Neanderthals in their calculations and may be considered more reliable. However, to speak more cautiously, we're still uncertain on this score, too. DNA can't resolve everything, and present data analysis techniques and interpretations are getting mingled without any consensus on the conclusions.

Was it 100,000, 80,000, 65,000, or 50,000 years ago? The picture of humankind, including ancient humans, changes depending on the era. "The question of whether *H. floresiensis* ever encountered *H. sapiens* is one such example," says Dr. Kaifu. "The age of *H. floresiensis* as revised in 2016 would have been 50,000 years ago, going by the evidence of their stone tools, or 60,000 years ago based on fossil evidence. If we trust those estimates, it would indicate that *H. sapiens* would have overlapped with *H. floresiensis* had *H. sapiens* arrived on Flores 100,000 years ago, whereas they would have only briefly encountered one another if *H. sapiens* arrived 50,000 years ago. I also think it possible they never met at all." Many different possibilities remain open, including the possibility that there was no overlap and no contact. We must be patient, even as we eagerly await future progress.

Were There Clashes?

One thing that still bothers me is that, however approximate the dating may be, there is no question that the advent of *H. sapiens* and the extinction of *H. erectus* occurred at the same general time. The question of whether our ancestors, *H. sapiens,* were directly involved in exterminating *H. erectus* troubles me no end. Just thinking about the scenario of *H. sapiens* fighting and eradicating *H. erectus* makes my heart ache. Maybe we would not exist in our present form if *H. sapiens* had not spread worldwide, but it would make me feel guilty indeed should our ancestors have been the terminators of a more diverse earlier world. I imagine those interested in this replacement hypothesis are motivated in part by just this sense of original sin.

"I get asked this question a lot," claims Dr. Kaifu. "Lots of people imagine a cruel, bloody scenario of some kind. But what I keep saying is that it was not necessarily like that. To take an example: if we say the common dandelion has outcompeted the native Japanese variety, it's not as though they're at war. In the case of animals as well, there is no need for direct conflict between them."

That helps. If you address the issue based on our knowledge of biology and ecology, this is true. When an invasive species drives a native species to extinction, the former displaces the latter by taking over its ecological niche rather than in direct battle.

Yet the historical record shows that we humans, we *H. sapiens*, have fought any number of wars. If we simply project this image on the past, then it may lead us to assume we fought with and exterminated other human species. That prehistoric megafauna like the woolly mammoth were hunted to extinction further contributes to that image. It seems there's a tendency within us that makes it easy for this image of blood-soaked ancestors to circulate widely. But in the absence of evidence, we do not need to think such cruel scenes played out.

Time Travel in Action

What sort of research can we anticipate will advance our understanding in the future? "The most basic thing would be new archaeological findings," says Dr. Kaifu. "There are still plenty of unknowns in Asia and much we don't understand in Southeast Asia. There have been many discoveries made recently, such as a report that old cave paintings in Sulawesi date back 40,000 years, on a par with similar works found in Europe. The world's oldest fishing hook, dating back some 23,000 years, has been found in Okinawa. More discoveries yet await in Asia. If we adopt a strategy of looking in certain locations because there are these specific things we want to know, then I think there is a high probability of success."

Dr. Kaifu also emphasized that, while excavating and carefully handling historical material remains the foundation of this work, new approaches may also be required. One specific example is a project to authentically recreate seafaring voyages from 30,000 years ago, for which Dr. Kaifu is the project leader. The concept behind this ambitious project is to verify how ancestors of the Japanese people, who first landed in Okinawa some 30,000 years ago, crossed the ocean from Taiwan, which at the time was still connected to the Asian continent due to the lower sea level. As it is believed people then didn't have the technology to control sails to navigate the passage using wind power, this effort required rowing by hand.

The project raised money in 2016 through crowdfunding and attempted to cross from Yonaguni Island to Iriomote Island on reed-bundle rafts. Many Japanese probably remember the experimental voyage, since it got considerable media coverage. The ocean current was unpredictably strong, running more than twice its usual speed, causing the boat to deviate from its intended course, ultimately necessitating that it be towed by its escort vessel. Even so, it was a first big step toward the eventual goal of voyaging from Taiwan to Yonaguni, with much learned along the way.

"Although there are archae- ological sites on these islands, simply digging them up doesn't give a sense of the ocean," said Dr. Kaifu. "For example, when it comes to what kinds of boats they might have used, the archae- ological sites have yielded no evidence, so the researchers sim- ply have no idea. There has been a tendency to just put the issue

Fig. 7-1: Holistic Reenactment Project of the Voyage 30,000 Years Ago: a study of Paleo- lithic seafaring by the first Japanese islanders. For details, visit the official website: https:// www.kahaku.go.jp/research/activities/special/ koukai/en/.

aside, as there's no way of researching it. Our approach is to say, all right, we'll try and do it ourselves for real, starting by building a boat using skills we can envisage our ancestors using as well as materials that were probably readily at hand. While the 2016 voyage was pulled offcourse midway through, it was nonetheless a significant effort. By trying to do it ourselves, we learned just how hard it is to cross the ocean."

For this first voyage, the participants cut down a marshy herbaceous perennial native to Yonaguni called *himegama* (narrow-leaved cattail). They then tied the reeds into bundles and lashed the bundles together to make their rafts. Even before venturing onto the water, they were hit hard at the boat-building stage by how much manual labor was needed. As they started paddling, the team members were forced to admit that "it was something ancient people accomplished but was too hard for us."

They set a goal in 2017 to go from Taiwan to an outlying island and made the trial voyage to the island on a raft of bamboo native to Taiwan, after confirming the wood could be cut down with stone tools like those used 30,000 years ago. This bamboo raft was the second candidate for the boat our ancestors might have used in their voyages. In the summer of 2017, the team members initiated another experiment using their third candidate—after the reed-bundle and bamboo rafts—a dugout canoe.

Through this try-and-see approach, Dr. Kaifu and associates have been seeking a new perspective on the great theme of the origins of humans as well as of Japanese people. If we think of digging up fossils at archaeological sites and contemplating them in the lab as time travel intended to draw the past to us, then this is an example of traveling into the past. It's an enterprise that quickens the pulse and stirs the spirit.

The group will once again raise money through crowdfunding, and after yet more research and experimentation, choose their best model boat for the voyages made 30,000 years ago. They plan to strike out in 2019 for their ultimate objective, a voyage from Taiwan to Yonaguni. Step by step, they will work to simulate the skills of their ancestors who crossed the powerful Kuroshio Current 30,000 years ago to reach the island. In replicating the voyage, they hope to learn firsthand what it was like for their ancient predecessors to attempt such a sea crossing.

Although there was no apparent change in the intensity he brought to the project, Dr. Kaifu had a different sort of passion when talking about this voyage than when discussing more conventional research. He seemed to have gained a real sense of the great advances that might be possible

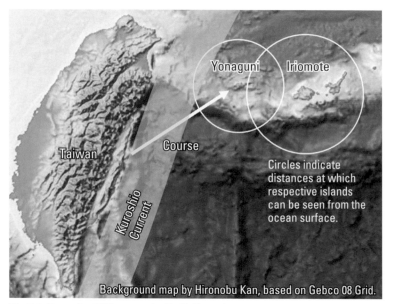

Circles indicate distances at which respective islands can be seen from the ocean surface.

Background map by Hironobu Kan, based on Gebco 08 Grid.

Fig. 7-2: Route for 2019 voyage by Dr. Kaifu and associates.

by using this new field of experimental archaeology. Such experiments, carefully planned on the basis of sufficient evidence, might become more important in times to come. For my part, I wonder if there will be people who make verification voyages—or verification drifts—to demonstrate how *H. floresiensis* might have reached Flores. I understand many research-ers think that, unlike the passage from Taiwan to Okinawa, the large num-ber of islands in the waters around Flores Island means that, depending on current directions, such a crossing wouldn't be especially difficult. Trying the voyage themselves might prove to be another matter entirely.

The Urge to Go

It's not terribly difficult to explain ancient diversity and modern homo-geneity. Leaving aside technical arguments about direct contact, we can broadly sketch the connection.

"Whether homogenous or diverse, the difference between *H. sapiens* and archaic *Homo* is that *H. sapiens* was able to go almost anywhere in the blink of an eye, relatively speaking," says Dr. Kaifu. "On the other hand, *H. erectus* and post-*erectus* grade archaic *Homo* could not, so they diversified, each adapting to its specific environment. *H. floresiensis* was stuck on their island. Java Man didn't make successive journeys to Flores. The same is true of animals as well. Late archaic *Homo* never reached the islands of Indonesia, which is why it is a place where *H. erectus* and *H. floresiensis* lived on and on. *H. sapiens* quickly reached Indonesia from the continent, yet late archaic *Homo* never did. Or perhaps it would be better to say, never could."

Listening to Dr. Kaifu's explanation, I felt as though a fog were clearing. That explains a lot. In no time at all, *H. sapiens* reached places that the older human species hadn't. *H. erectus* and likely their successors, late archaic *Homo*, had walked to the easternmost points of the Eurasian continent, but *H. sapiens* went farther. Groups with seafaring skills reached Indonesia, New Guinea, and Australia. Groups with the skills needed to survive in cold regions made their way into the far reaches of Siberia and eventually crossed the Bering Strait land bridge to spread out across the Americas. The homogeneity of *H. sapiens* is part of our ability to go wherever we want. Rather than significantly changing our form over long periods of time, we instead adapted by creating skills and technologies suited to each time and place, such as using sophisticated stone tools, deploying oceangoing boats, and wearing fur clothing.

This adaptability is in sharp contrast to the *H. floresiensis* ancestors confined to living on Flores who grew conspicuously smaller over the hundreds of thousands of years in response to their island environment. Java Man, too, underwent unique evolution after arriving on their island. Being isolated this way can be a significant cause of diversity. The same dynamic is operant in the emergence of many endemic animal species on isolated islands.

With sufficient creativity, we *H. sapiens* can go anywhere on the planet. Hence, our homogeneity. Rather than ourselves changing to suit the environment, we develop the tools and technology to change our personal environments to suit us.

H. sapiens are homogenous by having migrated across the earth in such a short geologic time and have become even more homogenous through continued genetic exchanges. Given recent advances in transportation, it seems such exchanges are still on the rise and that humankind is becoming more and more homogenous.

The Future of Homogenization

At this point, I'm aware of the danger of simply positing this as "diverse" vs. "homogenous" and "mobility" vs. "isolation."

In this twenty-first century, diversity is generally viewed as something positive. Biodiversity has long been a key concept in conservation, and diversity is also a keyword in discussions on social inclusiveness for minority groups. Though not necessarily a bad word choice, "homogeneity" seems to be perceived frequently as a problem if taken to extremes. For instance, education that promotes cookie-cutter homogeneity is now likely to be condemned. Conversely, the state of being isolated, which has given rise to the positive value of diversity, often has negative connotations. Of course, it's not possible to uniformly declare that isolation is a misfortune. But should you ask people which is preferable, many would choose freedom of movement to being isolated or confined to one place. Could this preference be due to our nature as *H. sapiens*?

And now that we've entered the twenty-first century, the trend toward ever greater homogeneity may be accelerating, especially in culture and the other software of our lives rather than in the hardware of our physical bodies. Thanks to advances in information technology, there are fewer limits to where we can go via data. We can get to know people on the other side of the world via social networks and speak with them via communication apps. We can search online for the latest scientific papers and get the most cutting-edge information. Seen from the perspective of the twentieth century in which I was born and raised, this world truly seems like a dream. On the other hand, the disadvantage of such freedom is that diversity can get lost and rich cultural heritages can become steadily impoverished, as seen in endangered languages spoken by linguistic minorities and facing extinction.

"That's the kind of world we're creating," Dr. Kaifu observes. "We ought to think through the possible negative impact, though the great historical trends toward movement, exchange, sharing, and homogeneity can no longer be stopped." Beyond the question of whether such trends bode well or ill, homogenization seems unstoppable. We are, after all, descendants of people who first dispersed over the continents and even crossed the seas to inhabit the whole of the planet.

The Final Frontier

Which brings us to the theme of space and the further spread of the human race. In late October 2017, immediately before finishing this book, I spoke with Dr. Kaifu about the issues to address in this final chapter.

Two weeks earlier, I had been in Adelaide, Australia, attending the International Astronautical Congress (IAC), the largest gathering of its kind. Nearly 5,000 attendees were there, from national space agencies to civilian aerospace interests, universities, and research centers.

While reviewing the book galleys and reporting on the conference, I felt as though I were working in two very different fields. Only now do I realize how connected they are.

SpaceX Founder and CEO Elon Musk gave the IAC final presentation. It was titled "Making Humans a Multi-Planetary Species." Since NASA retired the Space Shuttle, Space Exploration Technologies Corp., better known as SpaceX, has been at the forefront of the space development effort, sending resupply vehicles to the International Space Station and building the first reusable first-stage rockets—rockets that can return after launch and land on solid ground like something out of a science fiction movie. The near-future project for SpaceX is to establish a colony on Mars.

An interplanetary human diaspora, once the stuff of science fiction, is steadily approaching reality. Musk sketched out his plans in general

Fig. 7-3: Elon Musk talks of Mars colonization at the 2017 International Astronautical Congress.

terms to an almost fanatical response, ranging from how to reach Mars by 2020 to how to increase the livable space there after permanent settlement by terraforming the entire planet. He was treated like a rock star at this congress of space-sector greybeards including bureaucrats from the world's space agencies, sober university researchers, and private-sector executives.

This situation might well be similar to what *H. sapiens* experienced tens of thousands of years ago at the time of the first sea voyages. For some reason, we have been born with the ambition and the creative force to travel to unknown worlds. The moment we *Homo sapiens* developed oceanic navigation skills, we were living in places that had been out of reach for our predecessors: New Guinea, Australia, and even the Pacific islands. We may repeat those efforts in this twenty-first century in the form of building spaceships and traveling to other planets.

Will we continue to spread further as we become evermore homo genous? Or will we someday reach a point where we begin to diversify again? Where are the limits for humankind? Will the time come when we pass the baton to other sentient beings with an even vaster stage than our own?

Is Java Man Still with Us?

As I was finishing this book with my thoughts turned toward outer space and the future, Dr. Kaifu at the very last minute suggested one last possibility, one that both harbors the potential for deepening our consideration about the past and gives us cause for even greater excitement.

I received word that a new paper by Dr. Kaifu was scheduled for publication in December 2017—almost the same time this book would hit the shelves—in *Current Anthropology*, having first appeared in the magazine's online edition in November. The central idea of the paper was that modern humans may have interbred with Java Man (*H. erectus*). Dr. Kaifu argued that, just as with the interbreeding of Neanderthals and *H. sapiens* that has left traces in our genes, it may be that we also have Java Man genes in us. Though not yet an established theory based on accumulated evidence, this is a question Dr. Kaifu has raised for further investigation, one he has put on the academic debate table.

The first part the paper, titled "Archaic Hominin Populations in Asia before the Arrival of Modern Humans: Their Phylogeny and Implications for the 'Southern Denisovans'," delineates the diversity of humankind in

Asia, as also described in this book, and reconsiders genealogical relations, and the second part offers a new vision based on this latest interpretation.

Who Were the Southern Denisovans?

If you're wondering about the southern Denisovans in the paper's subtitle, that's very perceptive of you. Dr. Kaifu has set the label off in quotation marks and the southern Denisovans themselves are hypothetical.

Denisovans—without the "southern" appellation—have been mentioned elsewhere in this book. First announced by a German-Russian research team in 2010, they're an enigmatic ancient human lineage. We know from genetic research that Denisovans interbred with *H. sapiens*. However, the news that by far the largest amount of those genes are presently carried by the peoples of Australia and Melanasia, living a very long way from Siberia, was received with surprise.

The humans of these regions share as much as four to six percent of their genome with Denisovans. Why isn't this the case on the Asian continent, where the Denisova Cave is located? Why is this just in Australia and Melanesia, both very far removed from the Denisova Cave and separated from the continent by ocean? When and where could interbreeding of *H. sapiens* and Denisovans have occurred to bring about such outcome?

"The first thing that comes to mind as an answer to this mystery," says Dr. Kaifu, "is the hypothesis that Denisovans were distributed over the whole of Asia. One such Denisovan group in southern Asia interbred with *H. sapiens*, and thereafter their genes were transmitted to Australia and Melanesia. Some researchers have commented off the record that some late archaic *Homo* fossils found in China might also be Denisovans. However, no evidence indicates a morphologically uniform human species was once distributed from Siberia to Southeast Asia. If anything, the fossil evidence indicates quite the opposite, that numerous different human species were living in different parts of Asia."

This point has been made repeatedly throughout this book. It is an incontrovertible fact that various human species existed throughout Asia. Is there, then, yet another possible scenario that would not contradict this fact?

The main thrust of Dr. Kaifu's paper is that we should treat the southern Denisovans who transmitted their genes to Australian and Melanesian *H. sapiens* as distinct from the Siberian Denisovans of the Altai Mountains, that is, distinct from the main branch of Denisovans.

Fig. 7-4: Fossil sites of Asian archaic *Homo* as discussed in Dr. Kaifu's paper.

In this context, the term "Siberian Denisovans" (the main Denisovan branch) refers to an enigmatic ancient human species first unearthed in Denisova Cave. As noted earlier, they were found to share some four to six percent of their genes with modern Australians and Melanesians. While the DNA extracted from fragments of their bones and teeth has been recognized as a unique type, distinct from both contemporary humans and Neanderthals, we have little information about what they looked like owing to a lack of intact fossils.

The southern Denisovans—whom Dr. Kaifu, with his awareness of the diversity of ancient humankind in Asia, hypothesizes could have existed—are a human species different from the main Siberian Denisovan species, one that might have differed in appearance yet still shared portions of DNA owing to a common ancestor. As those genes are found in the *H. sapiens* group or groups that migrated to Australia and Melanesia, it would appear that Siberian Denisovans were somehow linked to this *H. sapiens* group in Australia and Melanesia.

Bumping into *H. sapiens*

With this in mind, let's consider anew where these southern Denisovans and the *H. sapiens* group in question might have met and mixed. "At this point, the thing to remember is that almost no Denisovan DNA has been found in groups of modern humans living on the Asian continent," says Dr. Kaifu. "This suggests interbreeding took place not on the continent but somewhere in the vicinity of what is now Indonesia, which would've been traversed en route from Asia to Australia and Melanesia. The interbreeding would have happened on the periphery of Southeast Asia, with the group bearing that DNA migrating to Australia and Melanesia. This would explain the curious geographical distribution."

The next question to ask would be what ancient human species existed in the vicinity of present-day Indonesia when *H. sapiens* arrived? As many of you have no doubt already realized, it would have been either Java Man or *H. floresiensis*. And if we take interbreeding between *H. sapiens* with *H. floresiensis* to be unrealistic due to the dramatic body and brain shrinkage in Flores Man, that leaves us with Java Man. In other words, as stated earlier, we may well be carrying genetic material from Java Man even today. This is Dr. Kaifu's bold new hypothesis.

Using highly detailed data, Dr. Kaifu has carried out research into the evolution of *H. erectus* in regions including Java, Flores, and Taiwan. We've looked at each of these. And the emergence of this great vision, the big picture of humankind in Asia, this scenic view of the history of humankind arising from a humble accumulation of facts and evidence, is itself an accomplishment worthy of special mention. But Dr. Kaifu waves us on even further, beyond even this vista. Having established a height from which humankind may be seen across Asia, he presents a dynamic history of humankind in Asia spanning two million years, however hypothetical it may be.

Tagging a Question Mark on Denisovan

Dr. Kaifu's hypothesis proposes a new way of viewing the identity of the Denisovans. "This is going to get rather complex and specialized," he starts, "but my paper draws attention to the problem that the Denisovans may not be a separate human group at all. That is to say, a group of Neanderthals, having migrated from the west to the region of Denisova Cave could have interbred with groups of either *H. erectus* or post-*erectus* grade archaic *Homo* native to the area and incorporated their DNA, which would have led to them being perceived as a new species of human."

In other words, suggests Dr. Kaifu, the humans we thought were Denisovans based on DNA findings might have been Neanderthals who had interbred. It's worth noting that fossilized bones determined by DNA analysis to be from Denisovans and those from Neanderthals were found

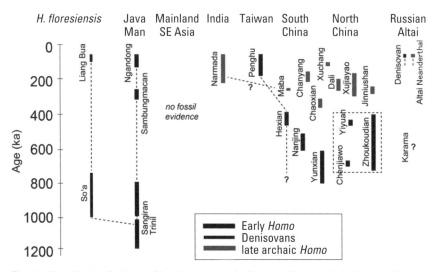

Fig. 7-5: Hypothesized relationships between early *Homo* and late archaic *Homo* in Asia as presented in Dr. Kaifu's paper.

in the same strata in Denisova Cave. A straightforward interpretation suggests they either took turns using these caves or shared the caves. Dr. Kaifu hypothesizes that the caves would've been occupied by one group, Neanderthals, among whom there must have been some with and some without genetic material from another archaic human group.

As an aside, Dr. Kaifu's hypothesis that the Denisovans may have been the product of interbreeding among ancient human species has also been raised by geneticists analyzing Denisovan DNA. Their scenarios are intricate and complicated, and Dr. Kaifu senses that "they don't seem very realistic and may be incorrect," so I won't go into detail about them. The views of geneticists on the cutting edge tend to get revised whenever new data becomes available, and there's no end to validation or discussion if you chase after every new announcement.

The Puzzle Pieces Fit

The scenario of possible interbreeding between Java Man and *H. sapiens* also shines new light on a debate which, though argued passionately some 20 years ago, now appears to finally have been all but wrapped up.

"It has to do with the morphological characteristics of the skulls of indigenous Australians," explains Dr. Kaifu. "Their skulls share a few similarities with those of Java Man, such as sloping foreheads and strongly protruding brow ridges. In the debates over the origins of *H. sapiens* at the turn of the century, these attributes were treated as a basis for the Multiregional Hypothesis of human origins. According to that hypothesis, indigenous Australians didn't trace back to Africa but instead evolved locally in Asia from Java Man.

"While we now know their ancestors were indeed part of the African diaspora, we're still left with the question of their skull characteristics. However, this point becomes explainable if there had been a little interbreeding with a Java Man group." I felt as if the pieces of a jigsaw puzzle had come together.

Of course, this is just one logical hypothesis about a significant enigma. In the years ahead, it will no doubt be thoroughly critiqued, tested, and its ultimate veracity determined. We have indeed come a long way: after all that work of going to excavation sites and minutely examining each and every discovered fossil, we not only have a map of humankind in Asia, but now the many human species depicted on that map have come to life!

We May Not Be Completely Alone

At this point, we have examined in detail not only the diversity but also the dynamism of humankind in Asia. In ancient times, there was striking diversity among humans in Asia. Then along came *H. sapiens*. They encountered one another in diverse ways and interbred. It's believed this involved interbreeding between *H. sapiens* and various ancient human species as well as with ancient humans.

The presence of many blank spots on the map where fossils are yet to be found suggests we're far from understanding the true diversity of ancient humankind in Asia. Neither the timing of *H. sapiens* arriving in Asia nor how long *H. erectus* survived is clear. And there's more that we do not yet understand about late archaic *Homo*. Instances may come to light in which—due to the inaccuracy of estimates made about when they lived—there was no contact between species. Yet the evidence derived from DNA has already shown a number of instances in which interbreeding did occur. The scenario of repeated contact and interbreeding among these populations fires my curiosity.

At the same time, however, I also feel profound peace of mind: I'd thought we were all alone, but it turns out that it's not just us, after all. All the humans who've come before are still living within us, still part of us. Just the sense of such a thing being possible makes me feel this species we call *Homo sapiens*, and by extension all of us, are boundlessly open to all things.

The debate over the origins of humankind doesn't merely satisfy our intellectual curiosity but is intimately bound up with questions of our own identity and how we perceive ourselves. Today, when our globally connected world is on the verge of becoming something truly universal, perhaps even cosmic, I want to understand what our past was like, what kinds of human species came before us, and who lives on within us. I can't help but feel the kind of anthropological research work presented in this book will provide a solid foundation for just such speculation as well as the strength to face our future.

Acknowledgements

I am grateful to Dr. Yousuke Kaifu, head of the Division of Human Evolution, Department of Anthropology, National Museum of Nature and Science, and his associates for their constant guidance on the journey of this book.

Any list of the many people who set aside time for me and allowed me a look into their fields would have to prominently include:

Dr. Akio Takahashi, associate professor, Faculty of Science, Okayama University of Science;

Dr. Reiko Kono, associate professor, Faculty of Letters, Keio University;

Dr. Iwan Kurniawan, Dr. Erick Setiyabudi, and Dr. Ruly Setiawan, all with the Centre for Geological Survey Geological Museum, Bandung, Indonesia; and

Dr. Fachroel Aziz, formerly with the Geological Research and Development Centre, Bandung, who continues his energetic field work.

I am profoundly grateful to you, one and all, and hope this book meets with your approval.

If I have shown readers a hint of the breadth of researchers at work as they painstakingly dig up fossils in the field, patiently confront specimens in the laboratory, and work to uncover new facts, together with that intellectual frisson obtained only in the course of discovery and inquiry, my intent in writing this book will have been achieved.

From the Technical Advisor

Looking around, it is pretty obvious the only humans alive today are *Homo sapiens*. But has that always been the case? And if not, what were things like before *Homo sapiens* came to dominate? These are some of the questions about human evolution in Asia that intrigued Hiroto Kawabata when he came to talk with me at the National Museum of Nature and Science in Tokyo. This book is the result of our discussions and more, and the writing gave him a ringside seat on many aspects of the research being done in Asia today.

I started physical anthropology studies in college in the 1990s, when human evolutionary studies focused almost exclusively on Africa and Europe. Extremely old human fossils were being discovered in Africa, and a great debate unfolded over the origins of humankind. Europe had classic and endless issues about who the Neanderthals and Cro-Magnons were and how they related. There was only limited interest in what happened in Asia. Asia seemed to be a backwater—a black box—as far as human evolutionary studies were concerned. Seeing this, and having been born in Asia, I resolved to become a researcher and shed what light I could on this Asian black box.

The first primitive humans to be discovered in Asia were *Homo erectus*, whose fossilized remains were found in Indonesia in the late nineteenth century. Then another regional group of *Homo erectus*, Peking Man, was unearthed in China in the 1920s and fossils of a more advanced but still primitive form of *Homo*, as well as early *Homo sapiens*, were found soon afterward elsewhere. Still, there was a long period devoid of any major finds in Asia, and our old awareness of these three types of humans remained unchanged for a fairly long time in the twentieth century.

Yet when you think about it, our tendency to focus on places where fossil remains have been found means that Asia's vast landscapes are untouched, unexplored, and rich in potential. There is a dazzling array of environments, from tropical to polar, and the mind dances at the prospect of the evolutionary diversity that took place here. There's much to learn about the history of human evolution in Asia, and we've only just begun to understand it. Indeed, there have been many discoveries of unexpected treasures since the turn of the century. This is the reality of Asian anthropology today.

It has been exciting to be part of this endeavor—doing field research and other studies on the story of humankind in Asia—and to have contributed a number of papers on this in English. Still, I feel a little guilty, being taxpayer-funded and having so little opportunity to share my findings with the general public. So I was delighted when Hiroto Kawabata, an accomplished author in his own right, showed up with his boundless curiosity and spot-on questions.

Because there were few Japanese engaged in the research, I was pretty much the sole resource for Kawabata, which might make the book appear to be a notebook of our research together. While this may be unavoidable, it is unfortunate, as there are many people of different backgrounds and countries doing physical anthropology in Asia today who contribute greatly to our understanding.

However, I hope this book about my work shows what I have learned, the surprises I have encountered, and the excitement I feel about its importance so that you will also be caught up in this quest to better understand where we came from and what might lie ahead for us. If you are interested in reading more, including some findings and speculation that weren't incorporated into the book, allow me to recommend my 2017 paper, "Archaic Hominin Populations in Asia before the Arrival of Modern Humans: Their Phylogeny and Implications for the 'Southern Denisovans'" in *Current Anthropology* 58: S418-S433. It can be downloaded free at https://www.journals.uchicago.edu/doi/abs/10.1086/694318.

Finally, I would like to express my profound appreciation to some of the many people who have supported me and cooperated with this research over the years. While it is impossible to list everyone, I am especially grateful to the following individuals (in alphabetical order by surname): Fachroel Aziz, Hisao Baba, Chun-Hsiang Chang, Noriko Hasebe, Reiko Kono, Daisuke Kubo, Iwan Kurniawan, Shuji Matsuura, Michael Morwood, Shuichiro Narasaki, Takashi Sano, Masako Shigeoka, Gen Suwa, Akio Takahashi, Masanaru Takai, and Kazumi Yokoyama.

Yousuke Kaifu
December 2019

From the Technical Advisor

Primary References

For Chapters 2 and 3

Baba, H., F. Aziz, Y. Kaifu, G. Suwa, R.T. Kono, and T. Jacob, 2003. "*Homo erectus* Calavarium from Pleistocene of Java." *Science*, 299: pp. 1384-1388.

Kaifu, Y., F. Aziz and H. Baba, "Hominid Mandibular Remains from Sangiran: 1952-1986 Collection," *American Journal of Physical Anthropology* 128, 2005, pp. 497-512.

Kaifu, Y., F. Aziz, E. Indriati, T. Jacob, I. Kurniawan, and H. Baba, "Cranial Morphology of Javanese *Homo erectus*: New Evidence for Continuous Evolution, Specialization, and Terminal Extinction," *Journal of Human Evolution* 55, 2008, pp. 551-580.

Kaifu, Y., I. Kurniawan, D. Kubo, E. Setiyabud: G.P. Putro, E. Prasanti, F. Aziz, and H. Baba, "*Homo erectus* Calvaria from Ngawi (Java) and its Evolutionary Implications," *Anthropological Science* 123, 2015, pp. 161-176.

Kaifu, Y., Y. Zaim, H. Baba, I. Kurniawan, D. Kubo, Y. Rizal, J. Ariz, and F. Ariz, "New Reconstruction and Morphological Description of a *Homo erectus* Cranium: Skull IX (Tjg-1993.05) from Sangiran, Central Java," *Journal of Human Evolution* 61, 2011, pp. 270-294.

Kaifu, Y., E. Indriati, F. Aziz, I. Kurniawan, H. Baba, "Cranial Morphology and Variation of the Earliest Indonesian Hominins," in C.J. Norton and D.R. Braun (eds), *Asian Paleoanthropology: From Africa to China and Beyond*, Springer, Dordrecht, 2010, pp. 143-157.

For Chapters 4 and 5

Kaifu, Y., H. Baba, I. Kurniawan, T. Sutikna, E. Wahyu Saptomo, R. Due Awe, T. Kaneko, F. Aziz, and T. Djubiantono. "Pathological' Deformation in the Skull of LB1, the Type Specimen of *Homo floresiensis*." *American Journal of Physical Anthropology* 140, 2009, pp. 177-214.

Kaifu, Y., "Furoresu Genjin *Homo Floresiensis* no Nazo" (The Homo floresiensis enigma), *Seibutsu Kagaku* (Biochemistry) 65, 2014, pp. 205-214

Kaifu, Y., H. Baba, T. Sutikna, M.J. Morwood, D. Kubo, E. Wahyo. Saptomo, Jatmiko, R. Due. Awe, and T. Djubiantono, "Craniofacial Morphology of Homo floresiensis: Description, Taxonomic Affinities, and Evolutionary Implications," *Journal of Human Evolution* 61, 2011, pp. 644-682.

Kubo, D., R.T. Kono, and Y. Kaifu, "Brain Size of Homo floresiensis and its Evolutionary Implications," *Proceedings of the Royal Society of London B* 280, 2013, pp. 1471-2954.

Kaifu, Y., D. Kono, T. Sutikna, E.W. Saptomo, Jatmiko, R. Due Awe, and H. Baba, "Descriptions of the Dental Remains of Homo floresiensis," *Anthropological Science* 123, 2015, pp. 129-145.

Kaifu, Y., D. Kono, T. Sutikna, E. Wahyo. Saptomo, Jatmiko, and R. Due Awe, "Unique Dental Morphology of *Homo floresiensis* and Its Evolutionary Implications," *PLOS ONE* 10(11): e0141614. DOI: 10.1371/journal.pone.0141614, 2015.

Van den Bergh, G.D., Y. Kaifu, I. Kurniawan, D. Kono, A. Brumm, E, Setiyabudi, F. Aziz, and M.J. Morwood, "*Homo floresiensis*-like Fossils from the Early Middle Pleistocene of Flores," *Nature* 534, 2016, pp. 245-248;

For Chapter 6

Chang, C.H., Y. Kaifu, M. Takai, R.T. Kono, R. Grün, S. Matsu'ura, L. Kinsley, and L.K. Lin, "The first archaic *Homo* from Taiwan" *Nature Communications* 6, 6037 doi: 10.1038/ncomms7037, 2015.

For Chapter 7

Kaifu, Y., M. Izuho, T. Goebel, H. Sato, and A. Ono (eds.), *Emergence and Diversity of Modern Human Behavior in Paleolithic Asia*, Texas A&M University Press, College Station, 2015.

Kaifu, Y., "Archaic Hominin Populations in Asia before the Arrival of Modern Humans: Their Phylogeny and Implications for the "Southern Denisovans," *Current Anthropology*, 2017.

Others

Kaifu Yousuke, Jinrui ga tadottekita michi: "Bunka no tayoka" no Kigen o Saguru (The Path of Humanity: Searching for the Origin of "Cultural Diversitification"), NHK Press, Tokyo, 2005.

Kawai Nobukazu, *Hito no shinka 700mannenshi* (seven Million Years of Human Evolution), Chikuma Shinsho, Tokyo, 2010.

Indo Michiko (ed.), *Jinrui daiido: Afrika kara Iisuta-toe* (Humankind's Great Migration: From Africa to Easter Island), Rinsen Books, Kyoto, 2012.

Indo Michiko (ed.), *Jinrui no idoshi* (History of human migrations), Rinsen Books, Kyoto, 2013.

Pääbo, Svante, *Neanderthal Man: In Search of Lost Genomes*, in Japanese translation by Nonaka Kyoko, Bungeishunju, 2015.

Kaifu Yousuke, *Nihonjin wa dokokara kitanoka* (Where Did the Japanese Come From?), Bungeishunjū, 2016.

Figure credits

National Museum of Nature and Science,Tokyo (pp. 34, 89, 94, 171)

Hiroto Kawabata (pp.13, 15, 16, 18, 22, 29, 40, 41, 47, 53, 56, 57, 58, 67, 73, 79, 80, 81, 100, 101, 102, 103, 104, 105, 107, 127, 129, 130, 131, 176)

Yousuke Kaifu (pp. 21, 24, 26, 29, 31, 33, 34, 69, 71, 72, 77, 83, 85, 87, 88, 109, 113, 120, 122, 134, 144, 145, 147, 148, 149, 154, 159, 162, 163, 173, 179, 181)

aflo (p. 40), Hisao Baba (pp. 43, 49, 59, 61, 75, 84, 85), Sakura Kougeisha (pp. 45, 48, 51, 87, 97, 126), GHR von Koenigswald Archive, Senckenberg Research Institute and Natural History Museum in Frankfurt/M. (p. 49), Sankei Newspaper (p. 96), Daisuke Kubo (p. 116) , Reiko Kono (p. 134) and Chun-Hsiang Chang (p.146)

Index

large teeth fossils (*Meganthropus*), 74

Fig. 3-6, Sangiran 6a (*Meganthropus* A), 75

Fig. 3-9, skull from Bukuran, Sangiran region, 79

International Astronautical Congress (IAC) 2017, 176

Fig. 7-3, Elon Musk talks of Mars colonization at 2017 IAC, 176

Space Exploration Technologies Corp. (SpaceX) planning colony on Mars, 176

Island rule

dictates physical size; big fauna grow smaller, small fauna larger, 98

small size of people on Flores due to adaptation to environment; lived there about a million years, 136

Stegolophodon (early elephant genus) shrank after land bridge submerged, 129

theory that *Homo floresiensis* evolved from early Javanese *Homo erectus* with island dwarfism, 114

Fig. 5-6, teeth of Flores giant rat, large due to island rule, 129

with dwarf animals, lived through many Ice Ages, 137

J

Java, Indonesia

geology and geography, 44

Fig. 2-6, map of, 45

part of prehistoric Sundaland, 161

Java Man

being X-rayed, 81

Fig. 3-20, changes in glenoid cavity in early, middle, late-skulls, 88

child's skull found at Mojokerto, near Surabaya, 46

cranial capacity, 27

dating Java Man, 166

DNA helps debunk Multiregional Hypothesis, 90

discovery 5, 14, 15, 26, 35

in Dubois Collection, Naturalis Biodiversity Center Museum, Leiden, 65

in the land of, 54–59

Fig. 2-16, Java Man diorama, Sangiran

Museum, 57

Java Man evolved, 71; fossils support out-of-Africa theory, 86

and specialization, 87; different from that of *Homo sapiens*, 90

Fig. 2-8, Java Man head at the Sangiran Museum entrance, 47

large teeth fossils, 74

jawbone in range of variation for *Homo sapiens*, 72

Fig. 3-3, lower jawbone fossils from Sangiran, 71

major fossil finds in Sangiran, 52

Fig. 3-21, main characteristics of *Homo erectus*, late archaic *Homo*, modern human skulls, National Museum permanent exhibit, 89

Fig. 3-15, main Java Man fossil skulls analyzed, support continuity, 83

massive bone extension above eye sockets of men and women, 56

missing link between apes and humans? 5, 14, 16

multiregional hypothesis debunked, 90

Netherlands, interest in, 40

rethinking brain size, 116

Fig. 3-16, sand on base of Sambungmacan 4 skull analyzed, 84

Sangiran 17 skull fossil and preserved facial bones, 46

skull first found by von Koenigswald, 50

skull found at Ngawi, near Trinil, 46

Fig. 2-5, skull fossil from Trinil, 43

skulls: indicate continuous evolution, specialization, terminal extinction, 82–87

sought by Dubois, 42

species evolved, not static in Asia, 70, 114

teeth change earlier in Java Man than in African *Homo erectus*, 74

teeth, jaws indicator of Java Man's evolution, 71–72

Journal of Human Evolution

detailed description (2009) of *Homo Floresiensis*, 108

Dr. Kaifu's findings (2008) on Java Man skulls, 82

About the Author

Hiroto Kawabata
Born in Hyogo in 1964 and raised in Chiba, Kawabata graduated from the University of Tokyo College of Arts and Sciences. He worked as a science reporter for the Nippon TV news department before going independent in 1997. Among his works of fiction are *Natsu no roketto* (Rocket summer), *Ginga no warudokappu* (Galaxy Kickoff!!), *Kumo no ou* (King of clouds), *Kawa no namae* (River names), and *Aoi umi no uchuko* (Space port on the blue sea). Among his many non-fiction works are *Dobutsuen ni dekiru koto* (What zoos can do), *Uchu no hajimari, soshite owari* (Our universe: The beginning and the end), and *Hachi-jikan suimin no uso* (The myth of the eight-hour sleep).

About the Technical Advisor

Yousuke Kaifu
Born in Tokyo in 1969, Kaifu earned his Doctorate of Science from the University of Tokyo's Graduate School of Science. He is currently group head for the Division of Human Evolution at Japan's National Museum of Nature and Science, Department of Anthropology, and leads the hands-on project to reenact the voyage to Japan 30,000 years ago. He was awarded the 2012 Japan Society for the Promotion of Science Prize for his research on Java Man and Flores Man. A prolific contributor to the scientific literature, he has also authored *Jinrui ga tadottekita michi* (Origins of humanity).

（英文版）
我々はなぜ我々だけなのか
アジアから消えた多様な「人類」たち
Lost in Evolution: Exploring Humanity's Path in Asia

2020年3月27日　第 1 刷発行

著　者	川端裕人
監　修	海部陽介
訳　者	デーナ・ルイス
発行所	一般財団法人出版文化産業振興財団
	〒101-0051 東京都千代田区神田神保町2-2-30
	電話　03-5211-7283
	ホームページ　https://japanlibrary.jpic.or.jp/

印刷・製本所　大日本印刷株式会社